BUILDING STONES OF EDINBURGH

"Edinburgh has long been advantageously situated in regard to good building stones"
(George Craig, *Transactions of the Edinburgh Geological Society*, Volume 6, 1893)

BUILDING STONES OF EDINBURGH

BUILDING STONES OF EDINBURGH

by

Andrew A McMillan
Richard J Gillanders
John A Fairhurst

2nd Edition

1999

Edinburgh Geological Society

Published by
Edinburgh Geological Society
c/o BGS, Murchison House, West Mains Road
Edinburgh EH9 3LA

First published in 1987
Second edition 1999

All rights reserved. No part of this publication may be
reproduced, sorted in a retrieval system, or transmitted,
in any form or by any means, electronic, mechanical,
photocopying, recording or otherwise, without the
prior permission of the Edinburgh Geological Society

ISBN 0 904440 10 9 (1999 edition)
ISBN 0 904440 04 4 (1987 edition)

© Edinburgh Geological Society

Bibliographic reference

McMillan, A.A., Gillanders, R.J. and Fairhurst, J.A. 1999
Building Stones of Edinburgh
(Edinburgh: Edinburgh Geological Society)

Designed by
Almond, East Cromwell Street, Leith

Printed in Great Britain by
Macdonald Lindsay Pindar plc, Edgefield Road, Loanhead, Midlothian

As the millennium approaches it is gratifying to find that the recent renaissance in the use of natural stone in the construction of Scotland's modern buildings is rapidly gaining momentum. In the capital city alone, the new National Museum of Scotland in Chambers Street, recent developments along the Western Approach Road and those in Lothian Road, ably show that adoption has gained ground. This level of acceptance has started to reverse the trend, increasingly evident in the first half of this century, to abandon natural materials in favour of energy-hungry and short-life, man-made products.

As the trend towards sustainability, energy efficiency and low maintenance costs gathers pace, there is a move away from a short-term approach to one which requires proven performance and durability for the medium to long-term. Life cycle costing considerations will inevitably be given greater prominence in this process and, with that, will come the increasing realisation that natural stone is a material that wins on every count.

Nowhere is this more convincingly shown than in Scotland's rich heritage of masonry buildings constructed before the turn of this century. The diversity, quality and achievement of this is well shown in our cities. The colour, texture and scale of the stonework plays a considerable part in creating local character and the individuality of each place.

Edinburgh is no exception and, having experienced the considerable personal professional gain from the first edition of *Building Stones of Edinburgh* on innumerable occasions, I was delighted to be informed that a new edition of this indispensable volume was being planned.

Following the scene-setting introduction, the reader is guided into the combined science of geology and art of architecture. The authors achieve an integrated translation of both successfully to bring together a seamless analysis and interpretation. This makes the building process come alive in a way that assists the viewer gain an interpretative ability that can be found in few places elsewhere.

This definitive guide ably and fully covers the range of stones used in the city. The reader is provided with all the key features that are required to become competent and knowledgeable in stone identification and appropriate usage. Supported by a choice of appropriate illustrations and case studies, the framework within which the various building stones were first formed is contextualised. The variety of supplying quarries are accurately placed in the appropriate geological time frame, system and formation. The inherent physical features that are to be encountered are described and explained and, from this, the basis for understanding how geology helps dictate architecture is formed.

The book is presented in a highly accessible form. It takes the lay reader on a detailed tour of the city in a way that brings the stones alive. Professionals are not ignored, and the text treats them to a succinct thesis of their predecessors' specifying abilities. This is impeccably researched and as a tool to aid appropriate specifying for ongoing repair and maintenance work, the volume is second to none.

This is an essential handbook for identification, decision-making or sheer pleasure, and it has been my privilege and delight to provide the Foreword for this Second Edition.

INGVAL MAXWELL, DA (Dun) RIBA FRIAS FSA Scot
Director
Technical Conservation Research and Education Division,
Historic Scotland

January 1999

CONTENTS

"The New Town is by far the most elegant part of the city.
It is laid out after a regular plan; and the houses being
all of modern, many of them contemporaneous erection,
constructed of the most beautiful materials, and of similar height, the effect of the whole is very splendid"

ROBERT CHAMBERS, 1825 (WALKS IN EDINBURGH)

Figures

Tables

PREFACE TO THE 2ND EDITION

In the decade since the first edition of *Building Stones of Edinburgh* was published the city has seen many new building projects. There have been many major new developments including those at Lothian Road, Castle Terrace, the Museum of Scotland at the head of Chambers Street and office blocks such as the Scottish Widows headquarters in Morrison Street. Other building developments such as those in Holyrood Road are embryonic. Currently the Scott Monument is under wraps whilst undergoing extensive repair and restoration. Throughout the city there has been an increasing use of stone for restoration and repair. There is thus an ever increasing need for information both on stone formerly used and that available today so that materials may be properly matched and appropriately used.

This new edition of *Building Stones of Edinburgh* is an updated version with many more illustrations. It has been rewritten in part and presented in a new layout to help readers readily identify for themselves the individual character of stones used in the city. Key buildings where stone is best displayed are highlighted. Emphasis has been placed on the geological characteristics because they form the fundamental component of the stone's character. As it is the intention of the authors to maintain and update their listings of stone sources for Edinburgh's buildings they would always welcome new information.

The authors owe a dept of gratitude to numerous people. First and foremost they would like to pay tribute to the late Ian Bunyan, principal author of the first edition, without whose in-depth knowledge and understanding of stone the original building stones project, supported by the Edinburgh Geological Society, would have foundered. A legacy from Ian towards the costs of the second edition is gratefully acknowledged. Another co-author of the first edition, who died shortly before its publication, was the late Dr Alex. Mackie who placed much of our understanding of the use of stone into an historical perspective.

We are particularly pleased to thank Ingval Maxwell of Historic Scotland, and Richard Griffith of the Edinburgh New Town Conservation Committee, whose encouragement and advice throughout the revision has been an inspiration. We also acknowledge the support of Bob Heath, Stone Consultant, for his review of an early draft and of Harry Turnbull of Stirling Stone. Both have done more than most to stimulate the dimensioned stone industry in Scotland. We thank numerous quarry operators and suppliers of stone who have provided samples or who have allowed collection of material for testing. The use of test data from the Building Research Establishment and the Edinburgh New Town Conservation Committee is gratefully acknowledged. We thank Alistair Stewart, Stuart Horsburgh and Fergus MacTaggart of the British Geological Survey, for preparation of figures and plates. Specific acknowledgement is paid to the following organisations for permission to publish illustrations in the book:

The British Geological Survey
The City Art Centre, Edinburgh
Clark Stone Limited, Edinburgh
Edinburgh City Libraries
Historic Scotland
The National Library of Scotland
The Open University Press
The Royal Commission on Ancient and Historical Monuments of Scotland
John Wiley & Sons Ltd and Professor M E Tucker

The Edinburgh Geological Society gratefully acknowledges a grant towards the design costs of this publication from Edinburgh New Town Conservation Committee (now the Edinburgh World Heritage Trust).

The following are acknowledged for their assistance with the first edition:

Members of staff of the British Geological Survey, in particular the late Mr Ranald Elliot for much useful background information and advice; Mr Neil Hynd, Principal Architect, Historic Buildings and Monuments Department (Scottish Development Department); the Royal Society of Edinburgh and the Royal Museum of Scotland.

PREFACE TO THE 1ST EDITION

This book is the result of many years' research by Fellows of the Edinburgh Geological Society. It attempts to fill a small gap in the rich literature concerning the history and development of Edinburgh by considering building stones which have been used in the city. The nature, properties and source of stone are treated in a geological context and the methods and history of sandstone quarrying are described.

An initial attempt to catalogue and describe Edinburgh's building stone was made by a class under the guidance of Dr John Miller of the Extra-Mural Department of Edinburgh University in 1976. Much useful information was gathered by Mr Frank Stewart and Miss Marion Froude, members of the class. Thereafter, activity on the project waned. However, the Council of the Edinburgh Geological Society was keen to promote the work with a view to publishing a book on the subject and, in 1982, asked Mr Richard Gillanders to lead the project team. In its early days the team included Mr Ian Bunyan, Dr Alex. Mackie, Mr John Fairhurst, Mr Norman Butcher and Mr Norbert Pawlowski. They concentrated on sandstones since it was these, above all other types of stone which were exploited, particularly in the Lothians and Fife, for the building of the city.

The book is not intended to be an excursion guide although parts of it may be used in this way and the reader may also wish to refer to Ian Bunyan's chapter in the 2nd Edition of *Lothian Geology - an Excursion Guide* by A D McAdam and E N K Clarkson (Edinburgh: Scottish Academic Press, 1986). The aim has been to synthesise many, but certainly not all, aspects of sandstone building in the city. The authors have had to seek far and wide for their information, not only consulting archives but also making field visits to as many surviving quarries in Scotland as possible. Since sandstone has been brought to the city from as far away as Caithness and Derbyshire, the task of documentation has been considerable. The literature has been consulted where possible, but inevitably in a subject which spans the uncertainties of stratigraphical correlation (in relation to the geology) together with the difficulties of precisely identifying the source of stone in a building, there are bound to be misinterpretations. Whilst accepting responsibility for what they have written the authors and the editor trust that the errors of their ways will be kindly pointed out to them.

Whether or not the team embarks on a second volume, studying stones other than sandstone (for example, igneous and metamorphic rock from Scotland or imported material) used in the city, to some extent depends on the response to this publication and also of course, the authors' enthusiasm. It is to be hoped however, that, in an age of brick concrete and steel, this initial contribution may serve as a reminder of a natural resource which has been utilised to great effect over many centuries, and which should continue to be used so that modern work may harmonise with and enhance the world-renowned elegance of the city of Edinburgh.

REFERENCE TO BUILDINGS, PROPERTY OR LAND IN THIS BOOK DOES NOT IMPLY ANY PUBLIC RIGHT OF ACCESS.

Aerial view of the
City of Edinburgh from the west.
BGS Photograph D6048 (1998).
Reproduced by permission of the Director,
British Geological Survey.

CHAPTER 1 | THE CITY OF EDINBURGH AND ITS GEOLOGICAL BACKDROP

"...a dream in masonry and living rock"

RLS (PICTURESQUE NOTES)

The City of Edinburgh possesses some of the finest sandstone-constructed buildings in Europe. Set in spectacular volcanic scenery carved from parts of an ancient extinct volcano, which erupted some 300 million years ago, the city was endowed with excellent local sandstone resources. The construction of both Old and New Towns exploited these building stones, some of which, for example the famous Craigleith stone, were exported around the world. The original Old Town was built on small hills, overlooked by the crags of the largest volcanic remnant, Arthur's Seat and by Calton Hill, another part of the volcano. To the south of the modern city are the higher hills of the Pentlands, volcanic rocks of even earlier eruptions. Variation in resistance to erosion between these hard volcanic rocks and the contemporary softer sedimentary strata has resulted in a landscape of hills and hollows. During the last 1.6 million years, glaciers of the Ice Age further exploited the variable physical characteristics of the ancient bedrock. Ice of the last glaciation disappeared some 12,000 years ago leaving the bold scenery we see today.

The sedimentary rocks, in particular the top quality sandstone, provided the local natural resource so effectively exploited in the construction of Edinburgh's buildings. Expansion of the city, with the development of the New Town on the north side of the Nor' Loch beginning in 1760, offered exciting challenges to architects and builders alike. During the latter part of the 18th century the demand for quality stone, so readily available on the doorsteps of the city, reached its peak. Continued expansion of the city during the19th and early 20th century exhausted supplies of locally available material and led builders to look elsewhere, firstly in the Lothians and Fife and latterly to other parts of Scotland and Northern England, as transport systems including canals and railways developed.

The use of natural stone declined following the First World War as concrete started to gain the ascendancy. In the last 30 years this decline has to some extent been reversed with the recognition that, used appropriately, the natural product is not only aesthetically more pleasing but more durable, enabling architects to build on that unique character which is Edinburgh. The revival in the use of sandstone was required firstly to make good the ravages of two hundred years of exposure to Edinburgh's smoke-laden atmosphere and secondly to provide modern buildings that at least give the illusion that they are built of natural stone.

Interest in the sources of sandstone grew during the 19th century as architects and builders started to look for new material which matched the colour and physical properties of stone in existing buildings. The first detailed published account of

Edinburgh's building stones was written by George Craig (c.1852 - 1928), architect to the Leith School Board. His paper, published in 1893, 'On the building stones used in Edinburgh: their geological sources, relative durability, and other characteristics' (*Transactions of the Edinburgh Geological Society*, Volume 6) showed that, even then, when natural stone was much more widely used, it was difficult to ascertain the sources of stone. He commented that 'even now much trouble is entailed in finding out the quarries from which many of the modern buildings have been obtained'. Aware as he was of the incompleteness of his results, Craig hoped that his work would be a useful 'first contribution to a branch of practical local geology that has been but little investigated, though full of both economic and scientific interest'. The problems which faced Craig are still with us and few detailed records are kept even of today's use of sandstone. *Building Stones of Edinburgh* (first published in 1987) attempts to bring his work up-to-date.

In recent years there has been a noticeable resurgence of interest in the use of natural stone for construction and cladding. In Scotland the increasing use of sandstone for both repair and new build has encouraged both the opening of new quarries and the re-opening of long abandoned workings. Sometimes a quarry will be reopened for a short interval to supply material for a specific building project. Other quarries have a long history of more or less continuous working. Of some twenty stone quarries currently (1998) in production in Scotland about eight are producing dimensioned sandstone and six are working flagstone (laminated, fine-grained sandstones suitable for paving). These quarries together with several in England are supplying material for buildings and streetscaping projects in many Scottish towns and cities. The renewed use of sandstone can be seen in many major developments in the City of Edinburgh, and heralds a revival in the traditional use of this material which was once locally abundantly available from famous quarries such as those at Craigleith, Hailes and Craigmillar.

The book describes the geology of sandstones, their lithology, structures and stratigraphy, together with some of the spectacular fossils buried in them (Chapters 2 and 3). It looks at how their physical properties are examined by the civil engineer and describes some results of recent tests on sandstones which have been used in Edinburgh (Chapter 4). A brief description is provided of how stone was quarried and prepared for use in the past, together with examples of modern working methods (Chapters 5 and 6). Chapter 7 describes, in stratigraphical order, a selection of locally quarried building stones with well-documented examples of their use in Edinburgh's

buildings. Examples of the use of stones from farther afield, including some currently working quarries, are highlighted in Chapter 8. The locations of selected buildings
in central Edinburgh and a summary of quarry sources are shown in Figure 1.1 and
Table 1.1 respectively. A series of appendices provide additional information.★

Although this account concentrates on sandstones, reference is made to limestone
and to rocks of crystalline igneous (e.g. granite) and metamorphic (e.g. slate and marble) origin to illustrate their contrasting properties (Chapter 2). Scottish granites have
been popularly used for ornamental purposes, plinths and tombstones during the last
150 years but it is only in recent decades that both indigenous and foreign stones have
appeared in the city as cladding frontages of commercial buildings. The reader is recommended to obtain a copy of *Lothian Geology – an Excursion Guide* edited by A D
McAdam and E N K Clarkson (reprinted 1996 by the Edinburgh Geological
Society). In this publication the late Ian Bunyan wrote an excellent excursion guide
covering both sandstones and more exotic stones to be seen in the New Town.

The aim of the authors of the 2nd edition of *Building Stones of Edinburgh* is the same
as that expressed by Craig over one hundred years ago that the publication 'will form
a foundation on which to build a more complete record that may prove of value in
the future' and additionally that the attention of architects may be drawn to a valuable resource still available in parts of Scotland.

★ *Throughout the book building names are shown in* **bold** *print. Building numbers in square brackets, e.g.* [43], *refer
to buildings listed in Table 1.1. The locations of these buildings in the vicinity of central Edinburgh are shown on
Figure 1.1. These and additional buildings (un-numbered) are listed alphabetically in Appendix 3.*

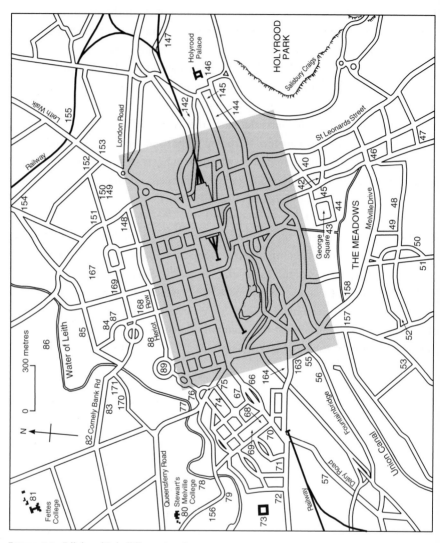

FIGURE 1.1A Edinburgh's buildings - location map

FIGURE 1.1B Edinburgh's buildings - location map (central Edinburgh inset)

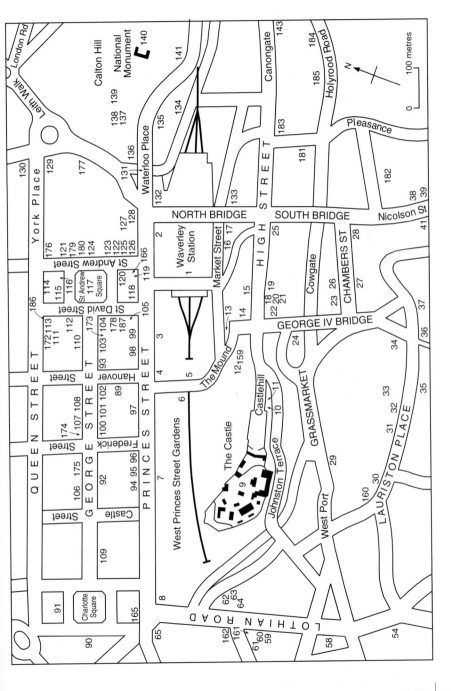

Table 1.1 Quarry sources for Edinburgh's buildings

Map numbers refer to Figure 1.1. Dates are the latest documented use of stone in the building. These and other buildings in Edinburgh are listed alphabetically in Appendix 3.

Map No.	Building name and address	Construction repair	Completion date	Quarry source
1	British Rail, Waverley extensions, North Bridge	Construction	1895	Woodburn Sands
2	Balmoral (formerly North British) Hotel, east end of Princes Street	Construction Repairs	1902 1991	Prudham Dunhouse
3	The Scott Monument, Princes Street	Construction Indents	1846 1975	Binny Clashach
4	Royal Scottish Academy, The Mound (Plate 7)	Construction Additions	1826 1836	Cullalo Craigleith Binny Humbie (West Lothian)
4	Royal Scottish Academy, The Mound, Queen Victoria Statue	Sculpture	1844	Binny
5	National Gallery, The Mound (Plate 6)	Construction	1859	Binny
6	Royal Scots Monument, West Princes Street Gardens	Construction	1950	Doddington
7	Scottish/American War Memorial, West Princes Street Gardens	Construction	1927	Ravelston No. 2
8	St John's, Princes Street	Construction Indents	1818	Redhall Stainton
9	Edinburgh Castle and The Shrine (17th to 20th century) Hall of Honour, National War Memorial	Construction Restoration Construction	1616 1619 1628 1639 1978 1927	St Cuthbert's Craigleith Maidencraig Craigmillar Clashach Doddington Swinton
10	Scotch Whisky Heritage Centre (formerly Castlehill School)	Margins Rock face ashlar	1896	Corncockle Hailes ('blue')
11	Tolbooth St John's Church, Lawnmarket	Construction	1844	Binny
12	New College and Assembly Hall, The Mound	Construction Paving and steps	1850	Binny Hailes Carmyllie
13	Bank of Scotland, The Mound	Construction Paving Indents	1806 1986	Binny Carmyllie Stainton
14	High Court of Justiciary, Bank Street	Construction	1937	Darney

Map No.	Building name and address	Construction repair	Completion date	Quarry source
14	David Hume Statue, High Street	Plinth	1997	Clashach
15	City Chambers, High Street	Construction	1761	Craigleith
		Additions		Longannet
		Construction	1904	Prudham
	Cockburn Street extension	Construction	1934	Darney
16	Cockburn Street	Construction	1864	Bishopbriggs
17	Scotsman Offices, North Bridge	Construction	1902	Prudham
			1979	Woodburn
17	City Art Centre, Market Street	Construction	1902	Prudham
			1970	Woodburn
18	St Giles Cathedral (High Kirk), High Street	Facing	1833	Cullalo
		Interior	1911	Cullalo
	Access to undercroft	Interior access	1984	Lazonby
19	Mercat Cross, Parliament Square	Restoration	1885	Hermand
20	Charles II Statue, Parliament Square	Plinth	1835	Craigleith
21	Parliament House, High Street	Freestone	1639	Burgh Muir
				Ravelston
		Rubble	1633	Society
		Façade	1810	Craigleith
22	National Library of Scotland, George IV Bridge	Construction	1955	Blaxter
23	Sheriff Court House, 27-29 Chambers Street	Construction	1997	Catcastle
24	Central Library, George IV Bridge	Construction	1890	Polmaise
25	Tron Kirk, High Street	Construction	1647	Society
				Craigleith
			1787	Craigleith
		Repairs	1976	Craigleith
				Darney
	Spire	Construction	1828	Humbie (West Lothian)
26	Crown Office, Chambers Street (formerly Heriot-Watt University)	Construction	1886	Prudham
27	Royal Museum of Scotland, Chambers Street	Indents	1986	Stainton
	Figures	Sculptures	1861	Doddington
	West wing	Construction	1889	Hermand
	Extension to south	Construction	1934	Cullalo
	Lecture Theatre, Lothian Street	Construction	1961	Blaxter
27	Museum of Scotland, Chambers Street, (Plate 12)	Cladding	1998	Clashach
28	Old College, The University of Edinburgh	Construction	1827	Craigleith
	Dome	Construction	1879	Grange
29	West Port Church (no longer a church)	Construction	1844	Hermand

Map No.	Building name and address	Construction repair	Completion date	Quarry source
30	Art College, Lauriston Place	Construction	1910	Closeburn
	Extension	Construction	1972	Locharbriggs
31	Lauriston Place, ground floor	Repairs	1981	Woodkirk
32	Vennel area, Bastion and Flodden Wall Figure 6.1a)	Construction	16th century	Burgh Muir Ravelston Hailes
33	George Heriot's School, Lauriston Place	Construction	1700	Ravelston Craigleith
	Interior courtyard	Rubble	1700	Craigmillar
	Additions	Additions	1920	Hawkhill Wood
34	Charity Workhouse, Forrest Hill (part only surviving)	Construction	1743	City
35	Royal Infirmary, Lauriston Place	Construction	1879	Hailes
	Extensions	Construction		Cullalo Longannet
	Jubilee Pavilion	Construction	1897	Corsehill
	Simpson Maternity Pavilion	Construction	1935	Blaxter
36	Medical School, Teviot Place	Construction	1886	Polmaise
37	McEwan Hall, Teviot Place (Plate 8)	Construction	1897	Polmaise Prudham
		Columns (2nd floor)		Corsehill
38	Surgeons Hall, Nicolson Street	Construction	1832	Craigton Cullalo Humbie (West Lothian)
39	Royal Bank of Scotland, Nicolson Street	Construction	1902	Corncockle
40	Nicolson Street, No. 82 (Figure 2.9)	Rubble work	Late 18th century	Salisbury (dolerite)
41	Nicolson Street Church (Civic Centre)	Indents and repairs	1986	Stainton
42	Buccleuch and Greyfriars Free Church, West Crosscauseway	Indents	1986	Stainton
43	George Square, west side: a few surviving buildings Most of the surviving buildings (including no. 20, Plate 3)	Construction Coursed squared rubble	1775	Craigleith Craigmillar with dolerite snecks
44	George Square Theatre	Construction	1967	Wellfield
45	George Square, east side: surviving early buildings, No. 60 (north-east corner of the square)	Construction Rubble	1779	Craigleith Craigmillar with dolerite blocks
46	Royal Dick School of Veterinary Studies, Summerhall	Dressings Rubble work	1916	Doddington Hailes

Map No.	Building name and address	Construction repair	Completion date	Quarry source
47	National Library of Scotland, 33 Salisbury Place, Causewayside	Construction Phase II	1987 1994	Newbigging Newbigging
48	Sciennes Primary School, Sciennes Road	Construction	1889	Hailes
49	Royal Sick Children's Hospital, Sciennes Road	Construction	1892	Corsehill
50	Marchmont Crescent, No. 38 (tenement)	Construction	1881	Clunevar
51	Arden Street area	Construction	1911	Blaxter Denwick
52	Warrender Park Crescent, Nos. 1-8	Construction	1881	Blair
53	Boroughmuir Secondary School, Viewforth	Construction Dressings	1911	Hailes Doddington
54	Methodist Central Hall, Tollcross	Construction	1901	Doddington
55	Fat Sam's (formerly Central Meat Market), West Fountainbridge	Construction	1890	Corncockle
56	Fountainbridge Telephone Exchange, Gardners Crescent	Construction	1952	Blaxter
57	Dalry Primary School, Dalry Road	Construction	1877	Hailes
58	Lothian House, Lothian Road — including stone relief of canal barge	Construction	1936	Blaxter
59	Film House, Lothian Road	Construction	1831	Redhall
60	Capital House, Lothian Road	Construction	1985	Woodkirk
61	Sheraton Hotel, Lothian Road (front only)	Construction	1985	Wellfield
62	Unitarian Church, Castle Terrace	Construction	1835	Cullalo
63	Saltire Court, Castle Terrace (Plate 10)	Construction	1991	Stainton Gatelawbridge (Newton)
64	Usher Hall, Lothian Road	Construction	1914	Darney Leoch
65	Caledonian Hotel, West End (Plate 11)	Construction	1903	Corncockle Locharbriggs
66	General Accident Assurance, Canning Lane, West End and 1-8 Atholl Crescent	Construction	1985	Dunhouse
67	Coates Crescent	Ashlar	c. 1820	Hailes
68	Palmerston Place, east side Nos. 15-21	Construction Indents	1880s 1985	Dalmeny Dunhouse Stancliffe
69	St Mary's Cathedral School	Construction	1885	Hermand
69	St Mary's Cathedral, Palmerston Place Spire	Construction Construction	1917 1917	Cullalo Black Pasture
70	Palmerston Place Church, West Side	Construction	1875	Polmaise
71	Coates Gardens	Construction	1876	Dalmeny
72	Magdala Crescent	Construction	1876	Dalmeny
73	Donaldson's School for the Deaf, West Coates	Construction	1851	Binny
74	Drumsheugh Gardens, Nos. 42 and 43	Construction	1877	Polmaise

Map No.	Building name and address	Construction repair	Completion date	Quarry source
75	Randolph Crescent	Construction	1820s	Redhall
76	Randolph Cliff tenement, northern corner	Construction	1849	Craigleith
77	Dean Bridge	Construction	1832	Craigleith
78	Dean Cemetery Wall	Dressed work Rubble work	1915	Woodburn Hailes
79	Hilton National Hotel, Belford Road	Construction	1978	Woodkirk
80	Daniel Stewart's and Melville College, Queensferry Road	Construction	1848	Binny
81	Fettes College, East Fettes Avenue	Construction	1870	Cullalo
82	St Stephen's Comely Bank Parish Church, 10 Comely Bank Road	Construction	1901	Corsehill Hailes
83	Cheyne Street, Nos. 15-19	Refacing	1984	Dunhouse
84	St Stephen's Church, St Vincent Street	Construction	1828	Craigleith
85	The Edinburgh Academy, Henderson Row	Construction	1824	Craigleith Cullalo Hailes Redhall
86	First Church of Christ Scientist, Inverleith Terrace	Construction	1911	Cullalo
87	Fettes Row, Nos. 30-31	Facing	1974	Clashach
88	Heriot Row No. 35	Construction Repairs	c. 1808 1998	Redhall Stanton Moor
89	Merchant's Hall, 22 Hanover Street	Construction	1866 1901	Dullatur Prudham
90	West Register House — formerly St George's Church, Charlotte Square	Construction	1814	Craigleith
91	Charlotte Square, north side (Figure 6.1g)	Construction	1795 after 1805	Craigleith Redhall
92	Freemasons' Hall — St Andrew Statue 96 George Street	Above plinth	1912	Pasturehill
93	Royal Society of Edinburgh, 26 George Street (former Commercial Union Building)	Construction	1909	Portland Stone (limestone)
94	Debenham's, 109-112 Princes Street	Construction above street level	1884	Polmaise
94	Debenham's, Rose Street	Construction	1884	Hermand
95	Marks and Spencer, 104 Princes Street	Construction	1980	Dunhouse
96	Royal Overseas League, 100 Princes Street (formerly Windsor Hotel)	Construction	1880	Dalmeny
97	Princes Street, Nos. 91-93	Construction	1960	Heworthburn
98	Dolcis, 70 Princes Street	Construction	1886	Corsehill
99	British Home Stores, 64 Princes Street	Construction	1965	Wellfield
100	George Street, No. 68	Construction	1955	Blaxter

Map No.	Building name and address	Construction repair	Completion date	Quarry source
101	Bank of Scotland, 66 George Street	Construction	1876	Dalmeny
102	George Street, Nos. 40-42	Construction	1984	Stainton
103	Dome Bar (formerly Royal Bank of Scotland), 14 George Street	Construction	1847	Binny
104	George Street, No. 2	Construction	1966	Heworthburn
105	Jenner's, Princes Street	Construction	1895	Cragg
	Rose Street	Construction	1890	Gatelawbridge
106	Bank of Scotland, 103 George Street	Construction	1885	Hermand
107	George Street, No. 65	Construction	1908	Doddington
108	George Street, No. 45	Construction	1974	Darney
109	Trustee Savings Bank, George Street, Nos. 120-124	Facing Paving in the entrance hall and atrium	1986	Dunmore (new) Ross of Mull (pink granite)
110	St Andrew's and St George's Church, George Street	Ashlar Columns	1784	Redhall Craigleith
111	Standard Life Assurance extension, Thistle Street	Construction Entrance paving	1964	Blaxter Spittal
112	Scottish Life Assurance Company, 2 North St David Street	Construction Entrance columns	1962	Springwell Wellfield Norwegian Larvikite
113	Stock Exchange, North St David Street	Construction	1970s	Stainton
114	National Portrait Gallery, Queen Street	Construction	1890	Corsehill Moat
115	St Andrew Square oldest buildings, Nos. 21, 22, 26	Construction	1772	Bearford's Parks
116	St Andrew Square, No. 28 and North St David Street (west side) (formerly Scottish Equitable Assurance) (Plate 9)	Construction	1899	Doddington
117	Melville Monument, St Andrew Square	Construction	1823	Cullalo
118	Old Waverley Hotel, 43 Princes Street	Construction	1887	Cragg
119	C & A Store, 33-38 Princes Street	Construction	1956	Woodkirk
120	South St Andrew Street, Nos. 10-18	Construction	1915	Blaxter
121	Bus Station (offices above entrance), No. 31 St Andrew Square	Construction	1970	Prudham
122	Royal Bank of Scotland (formerly National Bank of Scotland), No. 42 St Andrew Square	Construction Base	1936	Darney Rubislaw (granite)
123	Bank of Scotland, No. 38 St Andrew Square	Construction	1846	Binny
124	Royal Bank of Scotland, No. 36 St Andrew Square	Construction	1774	Ravelston
125	South St Andrew Street, Nos. 11-13, Job Centre	Construction		Wellfield
126	South St Andrew Street, No. 7	Construction	1886	Cragg

Map No.	Building name and address	Construction repair	Completion date	Quarry source
127	New Register House, West Register Street, East End	Construction	1863	Longannet
128	Register House, east end of Princes Street	Construction	1778	Craigleith Hailes
		Gallery construction Paving	1789	Craigleith Hailes
		Construction Paving	1820s	Craigleith Carmyllie Hailes
		Construction	1834	? Binny
129	St Mary's Roman Catholic Cathedral, Broughton Street	? repairs Repairs	1891 1978	Purdovan Woodkirk
130	St Paul's and St George's Episcopal Church, York Place	Construction	1818	Redhall
131	Regent Bridge arch	Construction	1815	Craigmillar
132	General Post Office (former), East End	Construction	1866 1890 & 1909	Binny Doddington
133	Trinity College Church, Chalmers Close (15th-16th century, rebuilt on present site 1872)	Construction	1872	Bearford's Parks
134	Governor's House, Calton Gaol	Construction	1817	Hermand
135	St Andrew's House, Calton Hill	Construction	1939	Darney
136	Waterloo Place, columns	Construction	1815	Craigleith
137	Dugald Stewart Monument, Calton Hill	Construction	1831	Humbie (West Lothian)
		Pillars	1997	?
138	City Observatory, Calton Hill	Construction Additions	1818 1895	Craigleith Binny
138	City Observatory House, Calton Hill	Dressings Rubble	1792	Craigleith Local volcanic rock and sandstone
139	Nelson Monument, Calton Hill	Construction	1816	Craigleith
140	National Monument, Calton Hill (Detail: Figure 2.8)	Construction	1829	Craigleith
141	Crown Office Buildings, Calton Hill (former Royal High School)	Construction	1829	Craigleith
142	Burns' Monument, Calton Hill	Construction	1830	Humbie (West Lothian)
		Indents	1978	Darney
143	Canongate redevelopment, Nos. 202-254	Construction	1966	Clashach
144	Milton House School, Canongate	Construction	1886	Corncockle Hailes ('grey')
145	Scottish & Newcastle plc, 111 Holyrood Road	Construction	1961	Blaxter

Map No.	Building name and address	Construction repair	Completion date	Quarry source
146	Holyrood Palace (mainly 16th century)	Construction	16th century	Barnbougle
				Broughton
				Craigleith
				Cramond
				Dumbiedykes
				Granton
				Leith Hill
				Niddrie
				Queensferry
				Ravelston
				St Cuthbert's
				Stenhouse
			1616	Craigmillar
				Salisbury
		Paving and steps	1983	Spittal
				Wellfield
	Fountain	Construction	1859	Binny
147	Elsie Inglis Hospital, Spring Gardens	Construction	1923	Cullalo
148	Broughton Street/Albany Street Office Development	Construction	1983	Stainton
149	East Broughton Place Church Hall	Dressings	1887	Corsehill
150	London Street School	Construction	1887	Prudham
151	Mansfield Place Church (formerly Bellevue Reformed Baptist Church), East London Street	Construction	1885	Plean Woodburn
152	Apex House, Haddington Place/Annandale Street	Construction	1975	Springwell
153	Brunswick House, Brunswick Street	Construction	1975	Woodkirk
154	Broughton Primary School	Construction	1897	Hailes
155	Buchanan Street Lane	Construction		Dunhouse
155	South Buchanan Street tenements	Construction	1881	Auchinlea
156	National Gallery of Modern Art (formerly John Watson's School), Belford Road	Construction	1825	Craigleith
157	King's Theatre, Tollcross	Construction	1904	Closeburn
158	Meadows West Commemorative Pillars and Sundial, West Meadow Park, Melville Drive (Figures 6.2-6.3)	Individual ashlar blocks	1886	Ballochmyle
				Binny
				Cocklaw
				Corncockle
				Corsehill
				Cragg
				Dalmeny
				Dunmore
				Gatelawbridge
				Gunnerton
				Hailes
				Hermand

Map No.	Building name and address	Construction repair	Completion date	Quarry source

158	Meadows West Commemorative Pillars and Sundial (continued)			Leoch
				Moat
				Myreton
				Parkhead —
				  (Woodburn)
				Plean
				Polmaise
				Prudham
				Redhall
				Whitsome —
				  Newton
				Woodburn

159	Free Church of Scotland College, Mound Place	Construction	1863	Hailes ('blue')
160	Fire Station, Lauriston Place	Construction	1901	Locharbriggs
161	Exchange Plaza, Lothian Road	Construction	1997	Dunhouse
162	Standard Life, Lothian Road	Construction	1997	Stainton
163	Scottish Widows Fund and Life Assurance Society Morrison Street (Plate 13)	Construction	1997	Clashach
164	International Conference Centre, Morrison Street	Construction	1996	Stoke Hall
165	Frasers Department Store, Nos. 145-149 Princes Street	Construction	1935	Heworthburn
166	Burtons, 30-31 Princes Street (formerly R W Forsyth)	Construction	1907	Blaxter
167	Royal Crescent, Nos. 8-11	Restoration	1979	Springwell
168	Howe Street, No. 39	Mouldings	1982	Spynie
169	Great King Street, Nos. 83-89	Mouldings	1982	Spynie
170	St Bernards Crescent, No. 1a	Indents	1982	Spynie
171	Leslie Place, No. 12	Indents	1982	Spynie
172	Queen Street, No. 8	Construction	1771	Craigleith
173	George Street, No. 10	Construction	1990	Catcastle
174	Edinburgh Solicitors Property Centre, No. 85 George Street	Construction	1990	Gatelawbridge (Newton)
175	George Street, No. 97	Restoration Central portico and indents	1980	Clashach Stainton
176	Paton Building/York Place, Nos. 1-3 (Plate 14)	Restoration	1998	Clashach
177	John Lewis extension, Leith Walk	Cladding		Stainton
178	St Andrew Square, No. 9, upper elevations: Street level:	Cladding	1962	Derbydene limestone Bon Accord (black granite)

Map No.	Building name and address	Construction repair	Completion date	Quarry source
179	Norwich Union Insurance Group, No. 32 St Andrew Square	Construction	1970	Prudham
180	St Andrew Square, No. 35	Construction	1781	Craigleith
181	St Mary's Street, No. 32	Restoration	1983	Stanton Moor
182	Lady Glenorchy's Church, Roxburgh Place	Construction	1913	Cullalo
183	Holiday Inn Crowne Plaza Hotel, High Street (formerly Scandic Crown Hotel)	Rubble and dressed work	1990	Dunhouse
184	Moray House Teacher Training College, Holyrood Road	Repairs	1970	Clashach
185	Chessels Court, Canongate	Construction	1969	Clashach
186	Queen Street, Nos. 2-3	Construction		Prudham
187	Abbotsford Bar, north side of Rose Street	Construction	1902	Gatelawbridge

CHAPTER 2 | THE GEOLOGICAL CHARACTERISTICS OF BUILDING STONES

'Geology is the fundamental science which determines not only the scenery of any region but also its architecture'

FRANK DIMES (IN J ASHURST AND F.G. DIMES, 1990).[1]

INTRODUCTION

Scotland is endowed with a rich variety of sedimentary, igneous and metamorphic rocks that have been used extensively as building materials over the centuries. The characteristics and properties of building stones are related to the geological origin of the material.[2] Thus many of Edinburgh's buildings constructed before the 20th century owe their character principally to the locally available material of sedimentary origin, namely sandstone. Igneous rocks were also used for some of the early buildings and as a prime source of good quality, hard-wearing setts. In the early days of building, field-stones, river beds and local outcrops of rock from which stone could be easily extracted provided building material. Much of this stone was used with little if any further dressing to form random rubble walls. In areas where suitable rock cropped out, quarries were developed and stone became established as the local building material. As the means of transporting stone, and as roads, canals and railways developed, it became economic to use a variety of stones from further afield for general domestic, industrial and commercial use.

SEDIMENTARY ROCKS

Sedimentary rocks are formed by the accumulation of sediment, undergoing natural compaction, dewatering and cementation over a long time. The process of sedimentation may take place in a variety of depositional environments, for example in deserts, rivers, lakes and seas. Common rock types include conglomerate, sandstone, siltstone, mudstone and coal. Sedimentary rocks also include salt, formed by the process of evaporation of lakes and shallow inland seas, and limestone, formed by the accumulation of calcareous organic remains. Sediments may vary in grain-size from clay particles ($< 1/256$ mm) to boulders (> 256mm). Many different grain-size classifications have been proposed. This book generally follows the geological (sedimentological) definitions of the British Geological Survey (Table 2.1).

Sediments may be derived from previously existing rocks, organisms and vegetation. Changes in the environment during deposition and variations in the incoming sediment produce layers or beds (Table 2.2) of rocks of differing characteristics. Minerals taken into solution by surface and ground water are re-deposited as precipitates or crystals, cementing the grains or fragments of sediment together. Progressive burial produces compaction in the sediment that eventually becomes lithified into rock. Shrinkage of the drying sediments and movement of the earth's crust create joints perpendicular to the bedding planes which separate the layers of rock. Thus the constructional properties and

Phi units	Clast or crystal size in mm log scale	Sedimentary clasts		Volcaniclastic fragments	Crystalline rocks Igneous, Metamorphic or Sedimentary
-8	256	Boulders	G	Blocks & bombs	Very-coarse grained
		Cobbles	R		
-6	64		A		
			V		Coarse-grained
-4	16	Pebbles	E	Lapilli	
			L		
-2	4	Granules			
-1	2	Very-coarse sand			
0	1	Coarse sand	S		Medium-grained
1	0.5 (1/2)	Medium sand	A		
2	0.25 (1/4)	Fine sand	N	Coarse-ash grains	
3	0.125 (1/8)	Very-fine sand	D		Fine-grained
5	0.032 (1/32)				
		Silt	M		
			U	Fine-ash grains	Very-fine-grained
8	0.004 (1/256)	Clay	D		

TABLE 2.1 BGS Grain Size Scheme
Based on Wentworth, C K. 1922. A scale of grade and class terms for clastic sediments. *Geological Journal*, Vol.30, 377-392.
Reproduced by permission of the Director, British Geological Survey. © NERC. All rights reserved.

characteristics of sedimentary rocks depend upon the particles, the cements and the spacing of the bedding planes and joints. The combinations of these widely varying factors produce a wide range of sedimentary rocks, many of which are unsuitable as constructional stone for building but may have other applications. For example some shales and mudstones provide the raw material for brick-making.

Sandstones

The dominant rock type used in Edinburgh's buildings is sandstone. Sandstones originate as unconsolidated loose grains of sand deposited on the seabed, in coastal and desert dunes, on beaches or by rivers. The grain-size of sandstone ranges in diameter from about 1/32mm to 2mm (Table 2.1). The composition of the grains reflects the composition of the source rocks and the physical and chemical resistance to weathering of the constituent minerals. The texture (grain shape – Figure 2.1, and sorting – Figure 2.2) of sandstones is affected by the mode of transportation of the grains, for example by water or wind.

The geological characteristics of shape and sorting apply equally to unconsolidated sediments and to their lithified (rock) equivalents. Wind is often a good agent for sorting the sand, so that the range of particle sizes is small (Table 2.1 and Figure 2.2): the

Bed thickness: geological definition	Architectural use	Notes
Very thickly bedded 1 metre -- Thickly bedded	Ashlar and sculpture	Beds may be massive (without internal lamination) or laminated
0.3 metre -- Medium bedded		Beds suitable for building may contain internal thinly bedded or laminated structure (e.g. flagstones)
0.1 metre -- Thinly bedded	-------------------- Sculpture panels; Paving	
30 mm -- Very thinly bedded	-------------------- Roofing flags; Floor tiling	
10 mm -- Thickly laminated	--------------------	----------------------- Individual laminations unsuitable for building
3 mm -- Thinly laminated		

TABLE 2.2   Terminology of bed thickness and typical architectural use

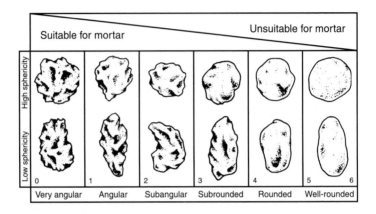

Figure 2.1 Categories of roundness for sediment grains and suitability for mortar
Adapted from *Sedimentary rocks in the field: Geological Society Handbook* by M E Tucker, 2nd edition (Chichester: John Wiley and Sons Ltd., 1996).

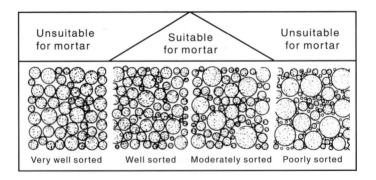

Figure 2.2 Degree of sorting and suitability for mortar
Adapted from *Sedimentary rocks in the field: Geological Society Handbook* by M E Tucker, 2nd edition (Chichester: John Wiley and Sons Ltd., 1996).

best-sorted sands tend to be those which have been transported and deposited by winds in deserts. These sands are also characterised by well-rounded grains. Note, however that a geologically well sorted sand is commonly considered to be poorly graded in quarry operator's terminology. When considering the suitability of sand for mortar it is important to assess both particle shape and degree of sorting. Generally angular, moderately sorted sands are best (Figures 2.1 and 2.2). A moderately sorted sand is considered to be well graded (i.e. with a normal particle distribution and median grain size of about 0.5 - 0.6mm).

Compositional maturity of a sandstone is defined by the constituent minerals which are determined by the source and agent of transport of the sand. Sands that are rich in chemically stable minerals, such as quartz (silica), are said to be mature. Sands with a wide range of mineral constituents, including a high proportion of clay minerals (complex silicates), are both texturally and compositionally immature. Sandstones suitable for use as building stone commonly consist of strong, chemically stable, particles of colourless quartz or light buff and pink feldspar. However the presence of particles of weaker minerals is not uncommon. An example is the flaky silicate mineral, mica, each flake reflecting light and giving a lustre to the fresh stone.

Bedding characteristics

The natural sequence in which sediments are deposited results in the youngest layer lying at the top and the oldest at the bottom (the 'principle of superposition'), providing the sedimentary pile is not disturbed or overturned by some external force. In building works it is often desirable to simulate this natural arrangement of sediment layers by laying stone 'in bed' and the 'right way up'. This is because the stone is not only better equipped to take imposed loads at right angles to its natural bed but also has the potential to weather better. When used in buildings, stratified stone is most resistant to compressive forces if laid with the bedding horizontal. 'The stone thus placed is best able to resist atmospheric disintegration and occupies in the artificial structure a similar position to that which it originally occupied in nature'.[3] There are circumstances, in the building of arches and corbels, where this arrangement is undesirable for structural reasons. Examples include edge bedded arch blocks in which the planar edge forming the length of each block is aligned parallel to the natural bedding. Each block is rotated a few degrees to form a curved arch. The visible surface of each arch block, thus exposes the natural bedding at an angle between horizontal and vertical. The extreme case where the block is laid 'on cant' with vertical bedding on the exposed face (also known as end bedding) is often seen in columns. Face bedded blocks, where the exposed face is parallel to the bedding, may suffer from de-lamination.

During the formation of the sandstone, the lapse of time between one layer of sediment being laid down and another is represented by a lateral discontinuity in the structure, known as a bedding plane, separating one bed of rock from another. Each bed can

Figure 2.3 Water-lain sandstone in Hailes Quarry, Slateford, Edinburgh
The fresh surfaces of rock clearly demonstrate characteristic wispy, black, carbonaceous, ripple laminae, a feature frequently seen in buildings constructed of this stone. The tools used included picks and wedges. The latter have been driven vertically into 'back' joints at the back of a bed. BGS Photograph C3114 (c.1926). Courtesy, British Geological Survey.

be sub-divided into smaller units and the thickness of the unit to be described as a bed may depend upon the context in which the term is used. Beds may be many metres in thickness but below an arbitrary lower limit of 10mm thickness the units are known as laminations (Table 2.2). Some medium- to thick-bedded sandstones have internal lamination which may render them unsuitable for polished ashlar but suitable for squared rubble work (e.g. Hailes Quarry, Figure 2.3).

Flagstones are laminated sandstones which split along bedding planes to produce slabs of uniform thickness up to 70mm. They have been quarried, mainly in the Northern Isles, Caithness and Angus for use as paving stones or roofing slabs. Many quarries in central Scotland supplied both thinly bedded sandstone for pavement and thicker beds for ashlar or rubble work. Hailes Quarry, for example, was noted for the production of laminated sandstone which was used extensively in Edinburgh for stairs, landings and paving stones. Other parts of the quarry yielded stone suitable for rubble work in walls. A freestone is a massive, medium- to thick-bedded sandstone in which no internal lamination is apparent and which can be worked with equal ease in all directions. Historically this was frequently referred to as 'Liver Rock'. Often, but not necessarily, the stone has a uniform appearance. The best unstratified stone from Craigleith, Edinburgh was described as 'Liver Rock'. However, it was a hard sandstone, difficult to excavate and dress. In the 19th century architects took much trouble, not only carefully to specify sandstones of varying bed thickness and durability, but also to note how they were to be used. This is exemplified by the detailed specifications recorded in the Director's Minute Book (1823) for the construction of **The Edinburgh Academy** [85], Henderson Row[4]:

'The whole Ruble stone will be got from Craigleith or Hailes Quarry. The Portico steps and whole landing within the Portico... and all the other stair steps and landings will be executed with the best Craigleith stone... The hearth of fireplaces and the Floors of the small entrance lobbies will be done with Dundee or Arbroath pavement, the whole ashlar work (Portico, Pilasters, mouldings, base etc.) on the principal front and East and West returns will be executed with the best liver rock from Collalo quarry; the remaining fronts being done with the best liver rock from Denny or Redhall Quarries....

The whole stone of whatever description used in the building must be laid upon their natural beds, and lime will be mixed up with clean sharp pit sand and pure fresh water. The whole walls and ceilings in the building will be finished with three coat plaster... The plaster lime must all be mixed with hair of the best quality, and be prepared at least six weeks before it is laid on the walls...

The lead used in every part of the work must be cast and all of the best quality. The whole roofs of all the buildings will be covered with the best Welsh Queen slates, hung with malleable iron nails, steeped in linseed oil when hot and laid on a shouldering of haired lime...'

Sedimentary structures in sandstones

Water- or air-borne particles are subject to physical laws which determine how they are transported and deposited. In a river, for example, cobbles and pebbles (the bedload) may be rolled or bounced along the floor of a channel. Finer sediments including sands may be transported partly as the bedload and partly in suspension. The finest sediments such as silts and clays will be carried in suspension. It follows that if the velocity of the current carrying the particles in suspension is high, only the larger and denser particles will settle; as the velocity drops successively smaller and less dense particles settle. Assuming that the current wanes uniformly, the resultant sediments will exhibit graded bedding, the particles in the bed grading from coarse at the bottom to fine at the top. Features such as graded bedding observed in sandstones indicate that depositional processes millions of years ago were the same as those today. Comparisons can be made with many easily observed modern sedimentary structures. For example, ripples, similar to those seen on beaches today, are seen preserved in ancient sandstones and their wave-like structures can be seen in vertical section as well as on exposed bedding planes.

Wave-forms on a larger scale occur in river channels and wind-blown sands, giving current-bedding (cross-bedding) (Figure 2.4) and dune-bedding (Figures 2.5 to 2.7). Often such features may be seen in ashlar blocks (Figure 2.4g) and provide an interesting and aesthetically pleasing structural component to the character of the stone. The

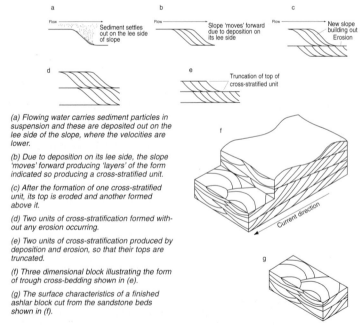

(a) Flowing water carries sediment particles in suspension and these are deposited out on the lee side of the slope, where the velocities are lower.

(b) Due to deposition on its lee side, the slope 'moves' forward producing 'layers' of the form indicated so producing a cross-stratified unit.

(c) After the formation of one cross-stratified unit, its top is eroded and another formed above it.

(d) Two units of cross-stratification formed without any erosion occurring.

(e) Two units of cross-stratification produced by deposition and erosion, so that their tops are truncated.

(f) Three dimensional block illustrating the form of trough cross-bedding shown in (e).

(g) The surface characteristics of a finished ashlar block cut from the sandstone beds shown in (f).

FIGURE 2.4 Sedimentary structures: the development of cross bedding in a water flow
Adapted from the Open University *Science Foundation Course units 26 and 27 Earth History 1 and 11* (1971, Milton Keynes: The Open University) and Bunyan et al., *Building Stones of Edinburgh*, 1st edition (1987, Edinburgh: Edinburgh Geological Society).

development of cross-bedding in water-laid sandstone is shown in Figure 2.4a-e. The tops of the waves are often eroded by the current which eventually deposits the succeeding layer, giving the wave-form a truncated appearance (Figure 2.4e). This enables the orientation of the stone to be determined because the individual sand layers will tend to become parallel to the base of the bed and truncated at the top. The three dimensional appearance of commonly occurring trough cross-bedding is shown diagrammatically (Figure 2.4f) and in a finished ashlar block (Figure 2.4g). Sometimes worm burrows are apparent, the 'tunnel' being filled with material which contrasts in texture and colour with the surrounding stone. Dewatering and slumped structures, which are commonly manifested as disturbed or convoluted bedding, may occur where quicksand conditions existed.

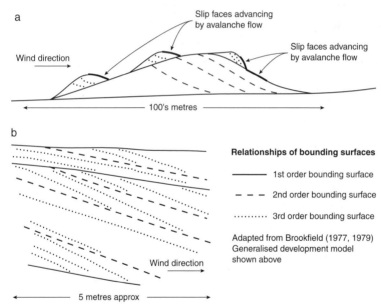

FIGURE 2.5 Sedimentary structures: section through an idealised large wind-blown sand dune
Adapted from Brookfield, M E. 1977. The origin of bounding surfaces in ancient aeolian sandstones. *Sedimentology*, 24, 303-332; Brookfield, M E. 1979. Anatomy of a Lower Permian aeolian sandstone complex, southern Scotland. *Scottish Journal of Geology*, 15, 81-96, and *Geology in south-west Scotland* edited by P Stone (1996, Keyworth: British Geological Survey).
The figure illustrates the formation of a dune and the development of bounding surfaces (see also Figures 2.6 and 2.7). The gently dipping side of the dune faces into the wind and sand grains are being continually moved upwards towards the crest (Figure 2.5a). The steep side of the dune is the site of successive avalanche flows as the dune migrates down wind. The large-scale cross -beds are the preserved foresets on the steep side of the dune. The wedge-shaped beds represent individual avalanches, each formed as a single event. Each dune was stabilised, then overtaken and eroded during the deposition of the subsequent dune, resulting in truncation at the top of the dune and the development of a 1st order bounding surface (Figure 2.5b). Very large dunes have smaller dunes migrating piggy-back over them, creating 2nd and 3rd order bounding surfaces.

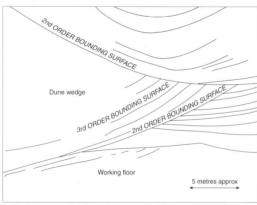

FIGURES 2.6 AND 2.7 Desert dune bedding in Ballochmyle Quarry, Mauchline

The view in Photograph C2193 (Figure 2.6) and interpretative sketch represents a small part (left of centre) of the working face shown in Photograph C2912 (Figure 2.7). It is part of a former very large dune composed of smaller migrating dunes. The three large wedges are bounded by 2nd order bounding surfaces (Figure 2.5b). The surfaces represent a period of time when the underlying dune was eroded, prior to deposition of the next dune. Within each wedge fainter laminations, 3rd order bounding surfaces (best seen in the middle wedge), converge downwards. These 3rd order bounding surfaces dip at angles in excess of 35° and flatten out as they curve towards the base of the unit. The size of sandstone block that can be hewn depends on the position from which the block is taken. For example thick beds may be worked from near the top of each major wedge defined by the 2nd order bounding surfaces.
BGS Photographs C2912 and C2913 (c.1921). Courtesy, British Geological Survey.

In dune bedding of desert sandstones the development of different orders of bounding surfaces (Figures 2.5 to 2.7) together with the joint spacing determine how the stone may be worked. The largest dimension of block which can be removed from the quarry platform is determined by the thickness of strata lying between bounding surfaces. In

urn this thickness is determined by the size of the successive sand avalanches involved
n the formation of the dune.

oints

The tendency for well-bedded sandstone to split along natural bedding planes is
exploited during quarrying operations. In addition to bedding planes the rock often has
two systems of joints or cracks almost at right angles to each other. One set of joints usually runs roughly parallel to the dip direction of the strata. In quarries which usually work
to the dip of strata, these joints typically cut into the face of the quarry and are known
as cutters.[5] The other joint system roughly follows the strike (i.e. at right angles to the
dip of the strata) and its planes lie parallel to the quarry face. These joints are known as
backs. Dip joints (cutters), strike joints (backs) and bedding planes give three natural
planes of division approximately at right angles to each other by which blocks of stone

can often be wedged out using a crow bar only. When the rock is very tough or the joints are very far apart, more powerful tools have to be used but even then backs and cutters usually define the shape of excavated blocks and the mode of development of a quarry.[6]

The geological jointing together with the bedding characteristics determine the size of block which can be quarried and dressed. In turn this dictates what size of stone block can be successfully used in a building. Thus the geology of the stone must be fully appreciated and employed in the ultimate build design.

Classification of sandstones: mineralogy, grain and cement composition and colour

The appearance (colour and texture) of a sandstone in a building is dependent upon the mineralogical composition of the stone. The mineralogy and composition of both the constituent grains and pore cement should be a prime consideration not only in specification of stone for new buildings but also in planning cleaning operations. For example the use of acidic treatments may etch grains, destroy pore cements and have a serious irreversible detrimental effect on the colour of the 'cleaned' stone.

Characteristics of sandstone which are observable with a hand lens both in the field and in blocks of a building enable a classification based on the mineralogy of the detrital grains to be used. The classification is defined by the relative proportions of quartz, feldspar and rock fragments (Table 2.3). Principal categories include quartz arenite, feldsarenite, litharenite and greywacke. Qualifiers based on the cement composition may also be used and commonly sandstones are described as siliceous (silica cement), calcareous (calcite – i.e. calcium carbonate cement) or ferruginous (iron-rich cement). A sandstone with high clay content may be referred to as argillaceous. Sandstones with a coal content are often described as carbonaceous.

The sandstones of Edinburgh's buildings are generally of fluvial or aeolian origin. Many of the local quarries yielded fluviatile quartz arenites, mineralogically mature sandstones composed predominantly of quartz grains cemented either with quartz or calcite. Typically, these sandstones appear almost white or pale grey at a distance. Some of the local sandstones are classed as litharenites which contain a proportion of a variety of lithic (rock) fragments. Stone within one quarry may show considerable variation in colour, texture, bed thickness, hardness and ability to resist weathering. The colour of the stone depends on the lithic fragments and carbonaceous material present. Sandstones with a high carbonaceous or argillaceous (clay mineral) content may be dark grey or brown.

Specific rock name	Mineralogical characteristics	Bedding and colour	Building sandstone characteristics
Quartz-arenite	Fluvial and marine sandstones: dominantly sub-rounded to sub-angular quartz grains; qualifiers define the cement content of the sandstone; siliceous sandstone (silica), ferruginous sandstone (iron-rich cement), calcareous sandstone (calcite or calcium carbonate cement). Argillaceous sandstones have a high clay content. Carbonaceous sandstones have a coal (organic) content.	May be massive (unbedded) or parallel bedded, planar and trough cross-bedded or laminated. Micaceous, laminated sandstones are referred to as flagstones; some sandstones are soft on working and harden on exposure; sandstones with calcite and silica cements are white or pale grey; ferruginous sandstones are brown and yellow; argillaceous and carbonaceous sandstones and flagstones are grey and brown.	Massive sandstone hard to work, may produce durable ashlar; bedded sandstones, particularly laminated stones including flagstones, may split easily; micaceous and carbonaceous laminae may enhance delamination especially in face-bedded blocks; iron-rich impurities may produce yellow and brown patterns; iron or carbonate nodules may give the stone a non-uniform appearance.
	Desert sandstones: rounded quartz grains coated with hematite.	Prominent dune bedding; often thickly bedded; shades of red; sometimes black laminae and streaks of manganese oxide may be present.	Spacing between bounding surfaces determines thickness of block; often soft to work, these sandstones produce ashlar blocks which harden on exposure.
Litharenite	Dominantly lithic (rock) grains.	Colour dependant on constituent rock fragments	Loss of surface skins and veneers may occur in sandstones with high clay content, leading to progessive weathering. Some clays absorb water leading to the decomposition of exposed faces.

TABLE 2.3 Geological and building characteristics of sandstones used in Edinburgh

Varieties of litharenites (argillaceous sandstones) are prone to failure through the loss of surface skins or veneers.

Stone colour variation can be well illustrated with reference to former quarries such as those at Hailes and Craigleith (see Chapters 3 and 7). At Hailes the lower beds, used for rubble work, were dark grey while the upper beds were of a pinkish hue and fer-ruginous. There was also a bed of 'blue-grey' rock and a small amount of stone suitable for ashlar. Other quarries could be relied on to produce stone of uniform colour, as at

Binny, Uphall.[7] The highly siliceous, massive, grey 'liver rock' of Craigleith may contain dark grey carbonaceous wisps, seen to advantage in the fine columns of the **National Monument** [140], Calton Hill (Figure 2.8) and **St Andrew's and St George's Church** [110], George Street.[8] Light coloured sandstones, worked at Ravelston (Chapters 3 and 7), sometimes contained ironstone concretions which, as well as being unsightly, weaken the stone when they weather out. In some modern quarries colour mottling, due to the presence of limonite is a feature of stone, seen for example in the light yellowish grey sandstone quarried from the recently reopened Newbigging Quarry, in Fife (Chapter 8). Clashach Quarry, Elgin currently yields excellent stone of colours ranging from orange to mottled brown for major developments in Edinburgh (Chapter 8; Plates 12 to 14).

Both the red sandstones from the *Kinnesswood Formation* (formerly 'Old Red Sandstone') of the Edinburgh district and the Permian 'New Red Sandstone' of Dumfries & Galloway and Cumbria (Chapter 3) owe their colour to the oxidising

FIGURE 2.8 Column of Craigleith Sandstone: The National Monument, Calton Hill [140]: detail
Note the wispy black carbonaceous laminae and occasional dark grey irony nodule (these are usually orchre-coloured) in the grey, very- fine-grained, sandstone.
R.J. Gillanders (1998)

regime of the semi-arid, desert conditions under which the sediments were originally deposited. Aeolian quartz arenites are often red through the presence of finely disseminated ferric oxide (haematite) which coats the grains. Only 1-2% iron is enough to produce strong colours.

Other types of sandstone (not seen in Edinburgh's buildings) include arkose (feldsarenites) and greywacke. Arkosic sandstones have a high percentage of feldspar grains that impart a pink or red colour to the stone. Greywacke is a hard, dark grey rock composed of principally of feldspar and lithic grains with a high percentage of clay matrix. Greywacke, commonly used in buildings of the south of Scotland and the Borders, owes its hardness and strength to low grade metamorphism that has affected the strata. These rocks can be durable but fracture irregularly. Such hard, dark stone has been commonly referred to as 'whin' in northern England and southern Scotland. Although whin is not used as a petrological classification, it was employed formerly by geologists as a field description for dark, compact, igneous rocks such as basalt and dolerite.

The strength of a sandstone is dependent largely upon the pore cement that binds the grains together. Generally, during the process of sedimentation, the pores (spaces) between the grains become partially or wholly filled by silica, calcite, clay minerals or iron oxides. In siliceous and calcareous sandstones silica and calcite respectively form strong bonds, although carbonate cements are liable to corrosive weathering, particularly in town atmospheres. Argillaceous sandstones cemented wholly by clay minerals are generally too weak to be used as building stone. Sometimes the sand grains remain virtually uncemented and the rock may be crushed in the fingers.

Weathering

The definition of weathering varies according to its usage in geological or masonry description. However, the geological make-up of a stone including its texture and grain and cement composition are important factors to be considered in both the natural and built environment. These characteristics may be observed both in a hand specimen and in larger structural units, for example quarry faces or ashlar masonry.

In the ground, a rock may undergo a series of weathering changes which can be classified according to the degree to which the strength of the material and the rock's mineral constituents are altered. Both physical disaggregation and chemical alteration may take place. The rock may be affected by changes in climate, burial, temperature and percolating solutions either from the surface or from depths in the earth's crust. The groundwater regime of circulating salt-bearing waters is critical. Movement of groundwater facilitates the transfer of chemicals in solution which in turn may interact with the rock constituents, affecting the strength and chemical composition of pore cements. Such processes may have acted on the body of rock for time spans of millions of years or over much shorter periods.

The relative hardness of interbedded sedimentary rocks can be observed in natural sections or quarry faces. Concentrations of flaky minerals such as micas on particular planes in the rock or variations in grain-size may reveal the natural layers or bedding formed during deposition which in turn may be exploited in winning the stone. Equally, internal planes or laminations within a single bed may be more prone to erosion. This may produce differential weathering of rock surfaces in quarry faces, natural sections and in masonry stone faces, particularly if stone is laid with beds 'on cant' (with bedding vertical).

In the built environment, stone is removed from its place of origin and regional groundwater setting and placed in an artificial position, either on the ground surface or at higher elevations. Freshly quarried stone is generally wet and full of 'quarry sap' and it is usually necessary to allow it to dry and season before it is used in a building. 'Stone that is quarried one day and built the next is in a green state, and unfit for use.'[9] Sometimes it is considered desirable to dress freshly quarried stone which is generally softer than its seasoned equivalent.   The hardening which seasoning brings to a stone may be attributed to the movement, in solution or suspension, of small amounts of siliceous, calcareous, clay or iron-rich material. This material is drawn to the surface by capillarity and deposited when the 'quarry sap' evaporates[10] and is thought to produce a kind of skin on the exterior of the seasoned stone affording some protection against weathering. However, there may be more to be said for firstly allowing stone to season, thereby allowing potentially damaging salts to be drawn to the surface before being removed by dressing.[11] Some local stone (e.g. from Redhall, Chapter 7) was soft when first quarried. This quality was noted for rendering the stone 'very fit for the chisel and delicate carving, and the more so as it hardens on exposure to the atmosphere and retains its polish long'.[12] Likewise Cullalo stone (Chapter 8) was particularly soft and friable but soon hardened on exposure.[13]

Although one stone type is often used, stone of different origin, texture and composition can be employed in wall courses. However the potential for chemical interaction between stones thus placed and between stone and mortar also needs to be considered in assessing the likely performance. Commonly occurring weathering of building stone includes the development of granular dissolution where surface grains become detached to effect a loss of sharpness in tooled faces and polished ashlar. Erosion patterns around

·dges of the stone may develop if there is interaction between the stone and lime mor-
ar. Delamination may occur where stone is laid 'on cant' due to the development of sub-
urface salt crystallisation or clay mineral expansion. Sub-surface salt crystallisation is par-
icularly noticeable in stones subjected to total saturation where zones of salt precipita-
ion cause efflorescence on drying out. Surface veneers and contour scaling may occur
rrespective of the natural bed alignment.

Limestones

Limestones are used as a major building stone in southern Britain.[14] In England, south
of the Humber, Jurassic limestones occur in thick beds and have been extensively
worked for dressed stone in the Cotswolds, the Bath area and Isle of Portland. Inevitably,
high transportation costs and local availability of good quality sandstone has precluded
common usage of limestone in Edinburgh. Portland Stone, a white shelly limestone of
Upper Jurassic age is commonly used in many English cities. A rare example of its use
in Edinburgh is the extension of the **Royal Society of Edinburgh**, No. 26 George
Street (formerly Commercial Union Insurance) [93][15] at the junction with Hanover
Street. Fossiliferous Carboniferous limestone from England has been used as cladding of
some buildings. Polished Derbydene shelly limestone from Derbyshire has been used to
clad the upper courses of **No. 9 St Andrew Square** [178].

In Scotland, limestone beds are generally too thin to be quarried economically for
dimensioned stone but have had a long history of usage, in the Lowlands and parts of
the Borders and Highlands, as lime for agricultural purposes, in mortar and as a flux for
iron smelting. Limestone was occasionally used locally in rubble construction with sandstone dressings and harling on vernacular buildings. Limestone has been mined and
quarried in the past locally at Burdiehouse, Middleton and Pencaitland in the Lothians.
Currently it is quarried in conjunction with shale at Dunbar for cement manufacture.

Limestone is formed by the accumulation of shells or the calcareous hard parts of
marine organisms, or by the precipitation of calcium carbonate as calcite, or the evaporation of water rich in minerals depositing crystalline calcium or magnesium carbonate.
During the Carboniferous Period, some 280 to 360 million years ago, the climate and
topography of the Edinburgh area were very different from that of today. A sub-tropical
climate and repeated invasion by shallow seas provided the environment for limestone to
form. Typically limestones and associated marine mudstones are fossiliferous, making
these rocks valuable for stratigraphical correlation.

The term marble, traditionally used by the building industry for any decorative limestone that will take a polish, is geologically restricted to recrystallised limestones. The latter contain new minerals formed in response to burial and heating of the rock at depths of several kilometres in the earth's crust (see Metamorphic Rocks - Marble).

IGNEOUS ROCKS

Igneous rocks, formed from hot molten source material known as magma, possess an essentially crystalline texture and are composed of small interlocking crystals of silicate minerals. Extrusive igneous rocks such as basalt are formed from volcanic or fissure eruption in which magma emerges through weaknesses in the earth's crust, producing irregularly layered lava flows that cool quickly in contact with the earth's surface and atmosphere. Locally, good examples of ancient basalt lava flows can be seen on Whinny Hill, Arthur's Seat. These rocks, together with tuffs and agglomerates (the pyroclastic products of the volcano), provided a ready source of building stone for the rubble work in buildings such as **St Anthony's Chapel** on Arthur's Seat,[16] the boundary walls of **Holyrood Palace** [146] and in the oldest walls of the **City Observatory House** [138] (built 1776-1792, to the specification of James Craig, designer of the First New Town[17]).

Intrusive igneous rocks of volcanic origin, such as dolerite, are the product of magma which fails to reach the earth's surface before solidifying. Some magma cools in pipes which feed volcanoes, forming plugs. Erosion of the earth's crust over millions of years exposes such rocks at the surface. The spectacular crag on which **Edinburgh Castle** [9] is built is an example where the surrounding sedimentary rocks have been eroded to deeper levels by ice-sheets. Magma also intrudes into natural planes of weakness within the existing rocks of the crust, forming thin sheets that are known as sills and dykes. A sill is an intrusion that lies parallel to the bedding planes of the sedimentary rocks which lie above and below it. The dolerite sill of Salisbury Crags, the prominent escarpment overlooking Holyrood Palace in Holyrood Park (Figure 1.1a), is a magnificent local example. It was here that James Hutton, (1726-1797), who inspired modern geological thinking, was able to show how the once molten magma had been injected into the surrounding sedimentary layers.[18] Dykes are planar bodies of igneous rock which have intruded across the principal bedding planes of the pre-existing rocks. When exposed by erosion, they often form wall-like features and are commonly relatively narrow bodies of rock, a maximum of only a few metres in thickness. Rapid cooling produces closely spaced joints, a characteristic which enables easy extraction but which limits the potential for using these rocks for dressed stonework. Such rocks are typically hard and intractable and thus are difficult to dress. Nevertheless, large quantities of durable dolerite were once extracted from Salisbury Crags both for 'calsey stanes' for roadmaking and for rubble work (see Chapter 7).

In Edinburgh the widespread use of stone of volcanic origin in rubble walling testifies to its local abundance and availability. Typically the common varieties of basalt and dolerite are dark grey to black rocks, composed of small interlocking crystals of feldspar and magnesium- and iron-rich silicate minerals. Andesite (found in the Pentland Hills), although similar in texture to basalt, varies in colour from pale pink to red. Dolerite produces typically tough but aesthetically uninteresting stone. Rarely, it has been used in the construction of old buildings such as at **No. 82 Nicolson Street** [40] (Figure 2.9) and in **George Square** [43, 45] (Chapter 7, Plate 3). Dolerite together with Scottish granite (see below) was quarried extensively in the past for use as setts for paving carriageways. Although granite setts are making a welcome return to many streetscaping projects

FIGURE 2.9 Nicolson Street, No.82 [189]
Rubble of local dolerite (possibly from Salisbury Crags).
R.J.Gillanders.

it is important to emphasise the use of appropriate base materials to prevent settlement and rock fracture. In modern times both dolerite and granite have been quarried extensively for crushed roadstone aggregate that provides rough-wearing surfaces.

Relatively slow cooling of bodies of magma at depths of several kilometres permits the formation of intrusive igneous rocks composed of large interlocking crystals of minerals (visible to the naked eye). Granite and black gabbro are common Scottish examples of these medium- to coarse-grained rocks (Table 2.1). Traditionally, granites were exploited in Aberdeenshire (e.g. Peterhead quarries – pink; and the quarries in and around Aberdeen - grey and pink) and Galloway (e.g. grey granites of Creetown and Dalbeattie). Granites from these sources (Figure 3.2) have been used in buildings throughout Britain and have been exported widely.[19] Even in Edinburgh, the 'Sandstone City', there are fine examples of Scottish granite work in buildings, plinths and monuments. The capability of granite to withstand large loads and ability to weather well has been utilised in the construction of plinth courses and for functional works such as bridges and docks. In Scotland granite is currently worked at Tormore Quarry, Ross of Mull and at Easter Delfour, Kincraig (Figure 3.2).

A general (geologically sensu lato) definition of granites embraces all medium- to coarse-grained, light-coloured igneous rocks with at least 5% quartz. Individual crystals should be discernible with the naked eye. Compositionally, granites contain between 55 to 75% silica. The mineralogy of the granite group comprises quartz and silicate minerals including orthoclase and plagioclase feldspar, muscovite (white) mica, biotite (black) mica and amphibole. The crystal size has a direct bearing on the purpose to which the stone will be used. Thus fine-grained varieties may weather better and be less liable to spalling in monumental and building work than coarse grained types. Porphyritic textures, in which large crystals, usually of feldspar, occur in a fine-grained groundmass tend to be of less value for setts and roadstone but can be used to striking effect in ornamental work. The large crystals display the variation in the natural colours of the rock's constituent minerals, a characteristic utilised to advantage in monumental work and for decorative purposes in buildings. Colours vary from grey to pink according the proportion of pink feldspar in the rock. An example is pink granite from Shap, Cumbria which can be seen in the columns of the portico of **St Mary's Cathedral** [69], Palmerston Place. Black biotite and dark green minerals such as amphibole may give a variegated appearance to polished granites.

Granites and a wide range of other medium- to coarse-grained igneous rock types, including many imports from overseas, have been used in recent years as polished cladding to concrete structures. In coarse-grained igneous rocks the cohesive texture of interlocking crystals prevents the plucking out of grains during polishing and enables a brilliant finish to be achieved. This contrasts with the matt finishes of 'polished' sandstone ashlar in which surface grains are more likely to be dislodged. The use of trade names, which may embrace many geologically different rock types, makes it a difficult task to determine the precise sources of these stones. An example is the Swedish black 'Bon Accord' 'granite' which has been used quite commonly in the city. At **No. 9 St Andrew Square** [178] (see above) polished 'Bon Accord' stone may be seen at street level. Inappropriate use of imported inferior rock types (e.g. the Portuguese granite recently used in the **Waverley Market** development (1984) is exhibiting noticeable pyrite staining) should be guarded against but should not discourage the use of good quality materials of either indigenous or foreign origin. There are many examples of imaginative use of imported rock types such as polished larvikite (a Norwegian syenite exhibiting a brilliant blue sheen), as in the superb columns which frame the entrance to the **Scottish Life Assurance Company** [112], 2 North St David Street.

METAMORPHIC ROCKS

When rocks are subjected to high temperatures and stresses deep within the earth's crust their physical characteristics may be changed. This process, known as metamorphism, produces crystalline rocks containing new minerals and exhibiting new textures. Although the rocks are often tougher and stronger than the original rocks they may be more brittle and susceptible to fracture. A wide range of metamorphic rocks can be formed according to the depth of burial in the earth's crust (in the order of tens of kilometres) and temperatures (up to 900° C) to which rocks are subjected. Although the texture and mineralogy of a metamorphosed rock are used to determine the degree (grade) of metamorphism, the mineralogy of the original material also has to be considered. The principal metamorphic rock type seen in Edinburgh's buildings is slate used in roofing. There are also many examples of polished marble for monumental and interior use.

Slate

For roofing, slates are the most commonly used low grade, fine-grained metamorphic rocks. They have been extensively quarried in Scotland, principally at Easdale and Ballachulish (Figure 3.2), Cumbria and Wales.[20] They commonly occur in varying shades of purple, grey and green and originate from mudstones (fine-grained sediments, which possessed natural bedding and lamination). When the mudstones are subjected to lateral compression and folded, new minerals, usually mica and chlorite form along planes normal to the direction of the compression and parallel to fold axes to develop slaty cleavage.

Slates usually split or cleave easily along this direction and sometimes the new minerals impart a sheen to the freshly cleaved faces. The process of metamorphism imparts a strength to the rock and the slaty cleavage, although rendering the material quite unsuitable for use as dressed stone, enables thin slabs to be split for roofing. Not all slates require to be cut to the same size and, in Scotland, a common practice was to use slabs of diminishing size on a roof, thus more fully utilising the available resource. Green and black slates are still available from Cumbria and are used for facing and paving as well as roofing. Despite a long and successful history of slate quarrying and the existence of suitable resources there are no currently operational Scottish slate quarries.

Marble

Other forms of metamorphic rock used for building stone, particularly for interior finishes include marbles. These rocks originate from limestones and their colour, mineralogy and texture are dependent on the composition of the original rock. In Scotland, marbles have been quarried on a small scale for ornamental and decorative purposes. 'Marble' has been used traditionally by quarrymen and stone masons to describe some limestones which are comparable as building materials to marbles, particularly in their ability to take a polish. True marbles are limestones which have been subjected to sufficiently high temperatures within the earth's crust to crystallise the rock, producing a tough, fine-grained stone which can be sawn and polished, providing an impervious and decorative surface.

Metamorphism of impure limestones has commonly resulted in the development of coloured marbles in which colourful silicate minerals such as serpentine minerals are present. Coloured marble, composed of serpentine and calcite, (the rock is geologically known as ophicalcite), was formerly quarried on Iona (the Iona Marble) and large quantities were sent to Leith and London.[21] Marble currently worked at Ledmore near Lairg (Ledmore North Quarry – Figure 3.2) is operated by Ledmore Marble Ltd. This stone commonly displays yellow, green and blue colour mottling, formed during metamorphism by the movement of mineral-rich fluids along small discontinuous joints. Block-size in the quarry is determined by the larger more continuous joints. Slabs can be cut to dimensions of a few metres, making the material suitable for panel work and interior floors. The floor of the entrance hall to **Longmore House** (Historic Scotland), Salisbury Place, is a fine example of polished Ledmore Marble.

REFERENCES

1. Ashurst, J. and Dimes, F.G., *Conservation of building and decorative Stone.* London: Butterworth - Heinemann. Volumes 1 and 2, 1990.

2. McMillan, A.A, *Quarries of Scotland.* Technical Advice Note No.12, Edinburgh: Historic Scotland, 1997.

3. Watson, J., *British and foreign building stones*, Cambridge: Cambridge University Press, 1911, p.9.

4. Magnusson, M., *The Clachan and the Slate: the story of the Edinburgh Academy.* London: Collins, 1974.

5. Smith, G., Account of the quarries of sandstone in the Edinburgh and Glasgow districts, and of the principal slate quarries in Scotland. *Prize Essays and Transactions of the Highland and Agricultural Society of Scotland*, (New Series) 4, 1835, p.90.

6. Greenwell, A., and Elsden, J.V., *Practical stone quarrying. A manual for managers, inspectors and owners of quarries and for students*, London: Crosby, Lockwood and Co., 1913, p.43.

7. Smith, G., *op. cit.*, 4, 1835, p.88.

8. Craig, G., Building stones used in Edinburgh: their geological sources, relative durability and other characteristics. *Transactions of the Edinburgh Geological Society*, 6, 1893, p.256-257.

9. *The Builder*, 1883, p.87.

10. Watson, J., *op. cit.*, p.11.

11. Ashurst, J., and Dimes, F.G., *Stone in building: its use and potential today.* London: The Architectural Press, 1977, p.25.

12. Carmichael, J., An account of the principal marble, slate, sandstone and greenstone quarries in Scotland, *Prize Essays and Transactions of the Highland and Agricultural Society of Scotland*, (New Series) 5, 1837, p.405.

13. Smith, G., *op. cit.*, 4, 1835, p.90.

14. Ashurst, J. and Dimes, F.G. *op. cit.*, Volume 1, 1990, p.86-118.

15. Craig, G.Y. in Gifford, J., McWilliam, C., Walker, D., *Buildings of Scotland, Edinburgh*, London: Penguin Books, 1984, p.24.

16. Land, D.H. and Cheeney, R.F. *Discovering Edinburgh's volcano: a geological guide to Holyrood Park.* Edinburgh: Edinburgh Geological Society. 1996.

17. McKean, C. *Edinburgh, an illustrated architectural guide.* 2nd Edition. Edinburgh: Royal Incorporation of Architects in Scotland. 1992, p.103.

18. Craig, G.Y. McIntyre, D.B. and Waterston, C.D. *James Hutton's Theory of the Earth: The Lost Drawings*, Edinburgh: Scottish Academic Press, 1978.

19. Ashurst, J. and Dimes, F.G., *op. cit.*, Volume 1, 1990, p.44-47.

20. *ibid.*, Volume 1, p.137-144.

21. Viner, D., *The Iona Marble Quarry*, The New Iona Press Ltd., 1992.

CHAPTER 3 | STRATIGRAPHY AND ORIGIN OF SANDSTONES USED IN EDINBURGH

"Stratigraphy is the study of the stratified or sedimentary rocks: their nature, arrangement, and correlation from place to place"

D. T. DONOVAN, 1966.[1]

Sandstones used in Edinburgh's buildings have been quarried not only in the Lothians and Fife (Figure 3.1) but also in many other parts of Scotland and northern England (Figure 3.2). The majority of quarries have long ceased operation. In some cases they have been infilled and re-developed so that little evidence remains today of their former extent. This chapter describes the locations and geological settings of both former and currently active building stone quarries and the stratigraphy of the sandstones worked. The information is summarised for selected quarries in Appendix 2.

GEOLOGICAL SETTING

Edinburgh lies within the Midland Valley of Scotland, an ancient rift valley or graben, bounded by two parallel faults, the Southern Upland Fault and the Highland Boundary Fault (Figure 3.2). The graben developed during the Devonian (410 to 360 million years ago) and Carboniferous (360 to 280 million years ago) periods and the resultant basin became a focus for sedimentation. To the south of the Midland Valley lie the mountains of the Southern Uplands formed by the folding, thrusting and uplift of greywackes and shales during the closure of a major ocean known as Iapetus. The mountain building episode is referred to as the Caledonian Orogeny. South of the Southern Uplands another series of major sedimentary basins including the Northumberland – Solway Basin formed during the Carboniferous period. North of the Midland Valley rise the mountains of the Grampian Highlands formed of ancient metamorphic and igneous rocks which have undergone several phases of folding and uplift.

In central Scotland the principal building sandstones were deposited as unconsolidated sands at intervals during the Devonian (the 'Old Red Sandstone') and Carboniferous periods. These and other sediments were laid down in a variety of depositional settings such as in rivers, deltas, seas and deserts. Detailed studies of the lithologies (composition and texture), sedimentary structures and fossils provide evidence for climatic changes as the surface of that part of the earth's crust which is now northern Britain moved northwards across equatorial latitudes.[2]

At various times during the Devonian, river sands and gravels accumulated to form a thick succession of sandstones and conglomerates in the southern part of the Midland Valley. Lake sediments (principally flagstones) formed in Angus. During Middle Devonian times the Caithness flagstones formed in a large lake covering part of northern Scotland and the Northern Isles. In the Midland Valley and northern England during the tropical Carboniferous period, volcanic eruptions punctuated the deposition of

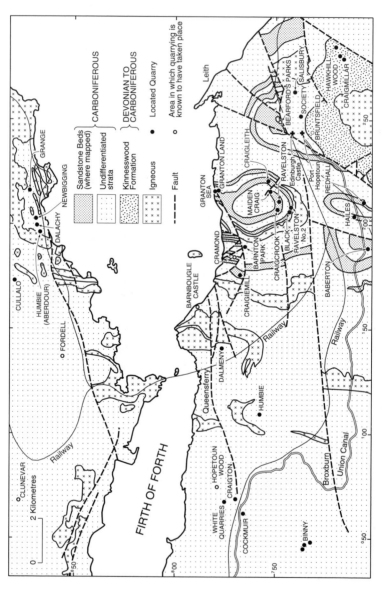

Figure 3.1 Edinburgh and neighbourhood: geology and sandstone quarries

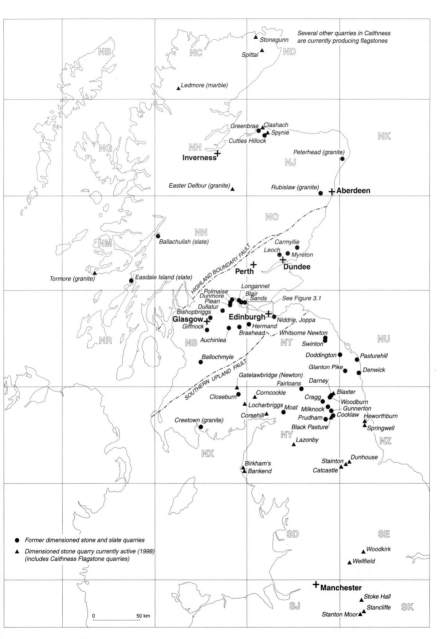

Figure 3.2 General locations of building stone quarries in Scotland and northern England
Lettered squares represent Ordnance Survey 100km National Grid.

thousands of metres of coal-bearing strata. Sequences of sandstone, mudstone, thin limestone, coal and ironstone were laid down in subsiding basins. Limestones and other marine fossil-bearing horizons mark periodic inundation of the land by shallow seas. The proportion and thickness of these component lithologies varied according to the conditions under which they were deposited.

Other sandstones used in Edinburgh's buildings are of Permian to Triassic age (280 to 210 million years ago). For much of this time desert conditions prevailed in Britain which occupied a latitude similar to that of today's Sahara. Consequently, the sands that accumulated to form the 'New Red Sandstone' were deposited mainly as large wind-blown dunes. Evidence for this is shown by sedimentary structures including aeolian (wind-blown) dune cross-bedding and the high degree of sorting and sphericity of the sand grains. Red Permian sandstones, much used as building stone, occupy small basins in the Vale of Eden, Dumfries & Galloway and Ayrshire. In Moray, Permian and Triassic buff and white sandstones were also laid down in an aeolian environment but close to the margin of a sea, conditions which effected unusual stone characteristics including convolute bedding and patchy silicification.

As a result of folding and faulting of strata deep in the earth's crust and subsequent erosion over millions of years, different parts of the sequence of sedimentary rocks are exposed today at the surface. Recent sediments, including the unconsolidated sands, gravels, silts, clays and boulder clays (till) of the Quaternary ice sheets (deposited during the last few thousand years) often obscure the solid rocks. However the relative stratigraphic positions of different beds of sandstone can be determined by combining evidence from geological field mapping and records of boreholes, mine and quarry sections. Studies of fossiliferous strata such as shell-bearing mudstone and limestone enable the correlation or matching of sedimentary sequences.

Tables 3.1 and 3.2 illustrate the principal formations from which sandstones have been worked. Formations are defined as sequences of strata that possess distinctive lithological characteristics. In central Scotland geological mapping by the British Geological Survey has enabled sandstones within these formations to be correlated between different quarries and outcrops. Typically sandstones from approximately the same stratigraphical horizon have been assigned local geographical names. Thus, for example, within the *West Lothian Oil-Shale Formation* the *Dunnet Sandstone* of West Lothian may be correlated with the *Grange Sandstone* of West Fife. At a higher level within this formation, sandstones quarried at Binny, Humbie and Dalmeny Quarries in West Lothian all belong to the same stratigraphical member named the *Binny Sandstone* (Table 3.1).

System/Series		Group (Gp)	Formation (Fm)	Quarries
TRIASSIC		un-named	Sandstones of Spynie	Spynie
		Sherwood Sandstone Gp	St Bees Sandstone Fm	*Corsehill
PERMIAN		un-named	Sandstones of Hopeman	*Clashach; Greenbrae
		Appleby Gp	Mauchline Sandstone Fm	Ballochmyle
			Locharbriggs Sandstone Fm	*Locharbriggs
			Thornhill Sandstone Fm	Gatelawbridge, Closeburn
			Corncockle Sandstone Fm	*Corncockle
CAARBONIFEROUS	Westphalian	Coal Measures	Upper Coal Measures Fm	Use of stone not documented
			Middle Coal Measures Fm	Auchinlea
			Lower Coal Measures Fm	Braehead
	Namurian	Clackmannan Gp	Passage Fm	Longannet, Blair; Sands
			Upper Limestone Fm	*Cowie Rock*: Polmaise; Dunmore; *New Dunmore *Giffnock Sandstone*: Braidbar *Bishopbriggs Sandstone*: Huntershill; Plean (Blackcraig); Dullatur, Local quarrying; Joppa
			Limestone Coal Fm	Clunevar; local quarry: Niddrie
			Lower Limestone Fm	Local quarrying
	Viséan	Strathclyde Gp	West Lothian Oil-Shale Fm	*Binny Sandstone*: Binny; Hermand; Humbie; Hopetoun White; Craigton; Cockmuir; Dalmeny *Grange Sandstone*: Grange; *Newbigging; Dalachy; Cullalo *Dunnet Sandstone*: Hopetoun *Hailes Sandstone*:Hailes; Redhall *Ravelston Sandstone*: Ravelston No. 2
			Gullane Fm	*Craigleith Sandstone*: Craigleith; Maidencraig; Barnton Park; Ravelston; Granton; Bearford's Parks and other local quarries
			Arthur's Seat Volcanic Fm	Local quarrying
		Inverclyde Gp	Ballagan Fm	Camstone, Dumbiedykes, Society
			Kinnesswood Fm (formerly classified as part of the Upper Old Red Sandstone)	Craigmillar, Hawkhill Wood; and local quarries including those in the Meadows and Bruntsfield area (the Burgh Muir) and Grange
DEVONIAN		Upper Caithness Flagstone Gp	Spittal Sub-Group (Middle Old Red Sandstone)	*Spittal and many other currently operational quarries (see Chapter 8)
		Arbuthnott Gp	Dundee Fm (Lower Old Red Sandstone)	Carmyllie; Leoch

TABLE 3.1 The stratigraphy of Scottish sandstones used in Edinburgh's buildings
(see also Table 3.2 for quarries in the Carboniferous of the Scottish Borders)
* Quarry currently (1998) operational.

System/Series		Group (Gp)	Formation (Fm)	Quarries
TRIASSIC		Sherwood Sandstone Gp	St Bees Sandstone Fm	*Bankend; *Birkhams; Shawk; Moat
PERMIAN		Appleby Gp	Penrith Sandstone Fm	*Lazonby
CARBONIFEROUS	Westphalian	Coal Measures	Middle Coal Measures	*Heworthburn *Woodkirk
			Lower Coal Measures	
	Namurian	Millstone Grit		Black Pasture; *Catcastle; *Dunhouse; *Stainton; Stancliffe; *Stanton Moor; *Stoke Hall; *Wattscliffe; *Wellfield
	Viséan	Middle Limestone Gp		Cocklaw; Gunnerton; Prudham; Purdovan; Denwick
		Lower Limestone Gp		*Woodburn; *Blaxter; Darney
		Scremerston Gp		Cragg; Milknock; Pasturehill
		Fell Sandstone Gp		Doddington; Glanton Pike; Fairloans
		Cementstone Gp		Swinton; Whitsome Newton

TABLE 3.2 The stratigraphy of sandstones from England and the Scottish Borders used in Edinburgh's buildings
* Quarry currently (1998) operational.

It is important to note that characteristics such as colour and grain-size can vary considerably within a sandstone from quarry to quarry or even between beds in the same working. A distinction should also be made between the stratigraphical (geological) name of the sandstone and the trade name because the latter may have been applied to stone of different origin and from different stratigraphical positions. Wherever possible, this account defines both the stratigraphy and the quarry from which stone has been obtained.

SCOTTISH DEVONIAN SANDSTONE ('OLD RED SANDSTONE')

During the Devonian Period the latitude of the Midland Valley is considered to have been sub-equatorial and the climate was semi-arid. Rivers which flowed principally during periods of torrential rainfall supplied large volumes of sediment to land-locked basins. Deposition of river (fluvial) and lake (lacustrine) sediments was preceded and periodically accompanied by outpourings of lavas from volcanoes, remnants of which form the Ochil Hills and Sidlaw Hills in the north and the Pentland Hills south-west of Edinburgh.

Sandstones of Angus

Within the Midland Valley, the Lower Devonian sedimentary succession is thickest in Strathmore, Angus where an estimated 7.5km of strata are present. The *Dundee Formation* (of the *Arbuthnott Group*), comprises a 1.5km thick accumulation of mainly medium- and coarse-grained, cross-bedded, fluvial sandstones with interbedded, fine-grained lacustrine sandstones (flagstones).[3] The latter were extensively worked for paving stones at Carmyllie quarries, near Arbroath, which supplied much stone for Edinburgh.[4] Blue-grey freestone from Leoch Quarry, north-west of Dundee, has also been used in the city.[5] Whilst in operation during the 19th century these and other quarries in Angus yielded an important assemblage of fossil fish and crustaceans[6] and plants.[7]

Caithness Flagstones

Strata of Middle Devonian age are absent in the Midland Valley but are extensively developed in Caithness and Orkney as flagstones (mainly laminated sandstones and silt-stones) which formed in a major lake. The flagstones are generally grey, demonstrating that a red hue is not ubiquitous to all strata of the 'Old Red Sandstone'. The total thick-ness of the flagstone succession in Caithness is 4km and in Orkney over 2km.[8] The sequence is made up of well defined rhythmic units or cycles of sediment, usually 5 to 10m thick, reflecting fluctuations in the lake level.[9] The cycles comprise, from top to base:

4. alternations of laminated siltstone and fine-grained sandstone
3. coarse, ripple-laminated siltstone often with very fine sand-filled syneresis cracks (formed under water in response to seasonal changes in salinity)[10]
2. laminated siltstone and shale
1. grey or black carbonate- and bitumen-rich, laminated siltstone with fish remains ('fish beds')

On account of their strength and ease of splitting Caithness flagstones have been used extensively as paving and roofing throughout Britain and abroad. The best flagstones for pavement are typically grey, interlaminated, fine-grained sandstone and siltstone. Currently, flagstones of the *Spittal Sub-Group* of the *Upper Caithness Flagstone Group*[11] are worked at several quarries including those at Spittal (Figure 3.3). These have recently supplied paving stone for some of Edinburgh's major streetscaping projects (Chapter 8).

Figure 3.3 Spittal Quarry, Caithness
A modern working flagstone quarry showing the flat beds excavated for pavement. A.A.McMillan (1984).

CARBONIFEROUS SANDSTONE OF THE MIDLAND VALLEY OF SCOTLAND

Britain's northward drift meant that by Carboniferous times sedimentation took place in equatorial latitudes. The Midland Valley of Scotland and the sedimentary basins of the Scottish Borders and Northern England contain evidence for rivers, lakes, lagoons and seas. Periodic rises in global sea level resulted in widespread marine conditions from time to time.[12] In eastern Scotland, former volcanic activity is preserved in remnants including Arthur's Seat, the Castle Rock and the lavas of the Garleton Hills, East Lothian.[13] The sedimentary rocks are arranged as a series of cycles or rhythms of different lithologies.[14] Principal rock types include coal, limestone, mudstone, siltstone, sandstone and fossil soil (seatearth). The proportion and thickness of these component lithologies varies according to the conditions under which they were deposited.

Inverclyde Group

The oldest Carboniferous strata in the Midland Valley are collectively referred to as the *Inverclyde Group* and comprise the *Kinnesswood Formation* and the *Ballagan Formation*[15] (formerly known as the Cementstone Group) (Figure 3.4).

Kinnesswood Formation

In the Midland Valley, uplift, folding and faulting of strata occurred during the Middle Devonian. Renewed deposition of river sands occurred during latest Devonian and earliest Carboniferous times. In Midlothian, around the Pentland Hills the estimated thickness of these sedimentary rocks, referred to as the *Kinnesswood Formation* (formerly part of the Upper Old Red Sandstone), is 640m.[16] Sandstones from this sequence were extensively exploited for early building work in the city. Local quarrying from the 16th century onwards took place at Craigmillar[17] and in the Meadows and Bruntsfield areas (the Burgh Muir) and Grange district (Figure 3.1) (Chapter 7).

Ballagan Formation

In the Edinburgh district the succeeding *Ballagan Formation* comprises sequences of interbedded sandstone, shale and cementstone (muddy limestone). The strata locally contain thin layers of gypsum and bands of nodular cornstone. This evidence indicates that the sediments were laid down in a coastal environment in which there were changes in water salinity, fluctuations in water table and periods of desiccation.[18] Sandstones from the *Ballagan Formation* were formerly worked in the Camstone Quarries,[19] east of Salisbury Crags on Arthur's Seat. They were also worked at Dumbiedykes, Society and many other quarries in the Old Town (Chapter 7). Dolerite of Salisbury Crags was also worked, primarily for setts.

Strathclyde Group

The *Strathclyde Group* includes the *Gullane Formation* and the *West Lothian Oil-Shale Formation* (formerly the Lower and Upper Oil Shale Groups).[20] The relative stratigraphical position of important building sandstones in these formations is shown in Figure 3.4.

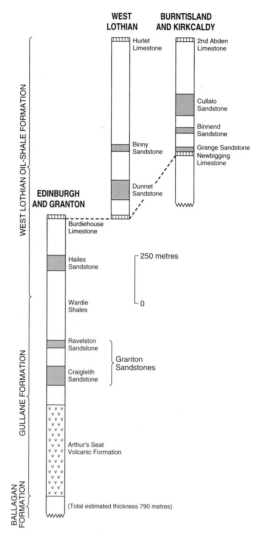

FIGURE 3.4 Generalized vertical sections in the Strathclyde Group of Lothian and Fife

Arthur's Seat Volcanic Formation and Gullane Formation

Lying stratigraphically above the *Ballagan Formation* strata are the *Arthur's Seat Volcanic Formation* and *Gullane Formation*. The *Arthur's Seat Formation* comprises a series of basaltic lavas, agglomerates, tuffs and intrusive rocks which, being generally harder than the surrounding sedimentary rocks, are an important component in Edinburgh's distinctive landform. Notable hills composed of these volcanic rocks include Arthur's Seat,[21] Calton Hill and the Castle Rock.[22]

The *Gullane Formation* of the Lothians and Fife supplied the bulk of Edinburgh's top quality building sandstone. The formation consists of a cyclical deltaic sequence composed predominantly of fine- to coarse-grained sandstone interbedded with grey mudstone and siltstone.[23] Rivers flowing from the north-east extended across eastern Scotland, supplying large quantities of sediment into the subsiding basin. Within this deltaic sequence thick, workable, sandstones are found.

In Edinburgh two principal stratigraphic units, namely the *Craigleith Sandstone* and the *Ravelston Sandstone*, have been extensively worked for excellent stone.[24] They are separated by about 90m of other strata and are sometimes collectively known as the *Granton Sandstones* (Figure 3.4). In west Edinburgh these sandstones form a circular outcrop known as the 'Granton Dome' or Granton Anticline.[25] (Figure 3.1). There were many early workings in the city centre but the principal supplies of the world famous *Craigleith Sandstone* were quarried in the Craigleith district (Figures 3.5 to 3.6; Plate 1) and at Granton (Chapter 7). During quarrying operations at Craigleith and Granton many fossil trees were recovered (Appendix 6).[26]

West Lothian Oil-Shale Formation

The *West Lothian Oil-Shale Formation* is characterised by a cyclical sequence dominantly composed of pale coloured sandstones interbedded with grey mudstones and siltstones. Within the upper part of the sequence the locally developed oil-shale seams (once economically-mined) are interpreted to have formed in freshwater lagoons in which abundant algae accumulated and putrified. These lagoons were populated by a remarkable fauna of crustaceans and fishes.[27]

Sandstones within this formation from local sources and from West Lothian and Fife have been used widely in Edinburgh. On the south-west outskirts of Edinburgh, the *Hailes Sandstone* (Figure 3.1 and 3.4) was worked at Hailes (Figures 2.3, 3.7 and 3.8) and Redhall. It was also quarried at Craigiemill near Cramond Brig and briefly at Baberton, but here a quarry, newly opened in the 1890s, had to be abandoned because the stone was so full of fossils as to be useless.[28]

Above the *Burdiehouse Limestone* (Figure 3.4), a non-marine limestone up to 15m thick, containing fossil plants, fish and ostracods, the upper part of the *West Lothian Oil-*

FIGURE 3.5 Craigleith Quarry, Edinburgh

This dramatic photograph shows the quarry at a time when the stone was becoming too expensive to work. The quarry is partially infilled with spoil. Thick massive beds of sandstone are exposed in the face beneath the pump engine house. In the background is a steeply inclined roadway. Photograph by Thomas Begbie (c.1850). Reproduced by permission of the City Art Centre, Edinburgh.

Shale Formation, is characterised by the occurrence of nine or ten oil-shale seams. The latter were formerly mined extensively in West Lothian. Two thick sandstones are present in this part of the sequence and were worked for building stone, particularly in West Lothian and in Fife. The *Dunnet Sandstone* of West Lothian, comprising mainly grey or brownish sandstones attains a thickness of 219m in the Deans and Livingston districts.

FIGURE 3.6 Craigleith Quarry, Edinburgh

Taken at about the same time as the Thomas Begbie photograph, this photograph, looking east, places the quarry in its setting on the western fringe of the city. Contrast the thickly bedded massive sandstone at the base of the quarry with thin overlying strata. Stewarts Melville College, built 1849-55 mainly of Binny Sandstone from West Lothian, is seen beyond the quarry with Edinburgh Castle and Arthur's Seat in the background. Photograph by W.D.Clark (c.1858). Reproduced by courtesy of Edinburgh City Libraries.

Quarrying in the *Dunnet Sandstone* dates back to 1697 at Hopetoun Quarry which provided stone for the building of Hopetoun House.[29]

The Fife correlative of the *Dunnet Sandstone* is known as the *Grange Sandstone*. It has been worked principally near Burntisland at Grange, Newbigging and Dalachy quarries. These quarries yielded large quantities of fine-dressed freestone blocks which were supplied to Edinburgh, Glasgow and Dundee as well as many parts of Fife. There is uncertainty as to whether the fine-grained, yellowish sandstone worked at the many Cullalo quarries[30] is correlated with the *Grange Sandstone* or is, as indicated in Figure 3.4, higher in the sequence.

Higher in the *West Lothian Oil-Shale Formation* is the *Binny Sandstone* which lies between the *Dunnet Sandstone* and the *Broxburn Oil-Shale* and was formerly quarried at ten localities in West Lothian and Midlothian. The most notable workings include those at Binny near Uphall; Hermand near West Calder; Humbie near Winchburgh; Hopetoun White, Craigton and Cockmuir quarries near Philpstoun; and Dalmeny.[31, 32]

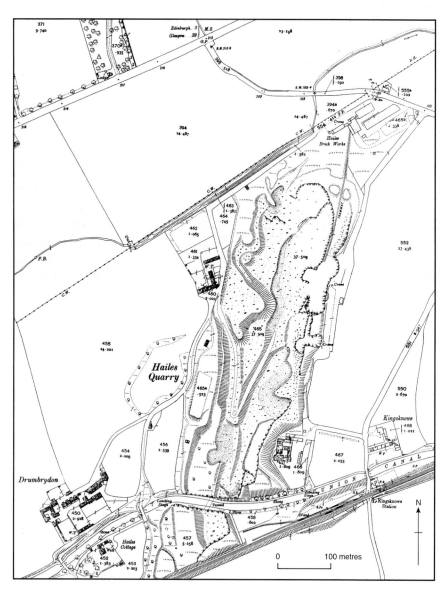

FIGURE 3.7 Hailes Quarry: Extract of the Ordnance Survey 25 inch County Map Edinburghshire III.13 and III.14 (1914 edition).
Note scale is reduced.
Reproduced by permission of the Trustees of the National Library of Scotland.

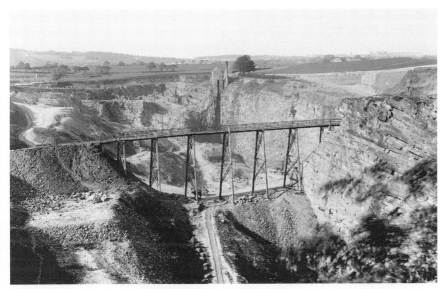

FIGURE 3.8 Hailes Quarry, Slateford, Edinburgh
General view of the quarry looking north, with the tramway bridge (not shown on the Ordnance Survey 25 inch County map, 1914 edition) and steam pumping engine in middle distance. Corstorphine Hill and Donaldson's Hospital are in the background. At this end of the quarry, the blue stone was more of a 'liver rock' in which lamination was not discernable.BGS Photograph B932 (c.1913). Courtesy, British Geological Survey.

Clackmannan Group
Lower Limestone Formation

Strata of the *Lower Limestone Formation* exhibit generally a marine lithology with rhythmic sequences of thin coals overlain by limestone, mudstone with marine shells, followed by sandstone. In the Lothians, sandstones have been worked for local building purposes[33] but have generally proved too soft to be considered for use as construction stone in Edinburgh.

In Fife, sandstone overlying the *Charlestown Main Limestone* of the *Lower Limestone Formation* was worked at Millstonemeadow Quarry,[34] near Otterston Loch east of Fordell Castle. The stone was said to have irony concretions which stained black on exposure.[35]

Limestone Coal and Upper Limestone Formations

Sandstones of the succeeding *Limestone Coal Formation* and the *Upper Limestone Formation* of the *Clackmannan Group* have been used in the main only locally for building

FIGURE 3.9 Huntershill Quarry, Bishopbriggs

The Bishopbriggs Sandstone was quarried and mined in Huntershill Quarry, Bishopbriggs. The sandstone is developed as two units, the lower part 18m thick and the upper part 14m. Mining by the stoop and room (pillar and stall) commenced in the 1850s as the overburden of poor quality strata and till increased in thickness. The galleries were some 15m high. The quarrying process was started by 'miners' who drove horizontal mines near the top of the post (bed). Quarrymen then wrought downwards from the mines, a few feet of solid sandstone being left to support the roof. Mining continued until about 1907 when a serious roof fall killed 5 men. BGS Photograph C2417 (c.1908). Courtesy, British Geological Survey.

stone. They were also used for furnace hearths, glass manufacture and for moulding purposes in the Lothians.[36] Local sources of stone from these formations were worked at Niddrie and Joppa respectively (see Chapter 7). The *Limestone Coal Formation* consists mainly of deltaic sequences of siltstones, mudstones and valuable coals with frequent channel sandstones. Sandstone of this formation brought to Edinburgh from Fife includes that from Clunevar, west of Dunfermline.[37] Coarse-grained, cross-bedded sandstones at the base of the *Limestone Coal Formation* were worked at several quarries near Fordell Castle.[38]

A significant group of building stones used in Edinburgh (and Glasgow[39]) is found in strata of the *Upper Limestone Formation* in west-central Scotland. In the Glasgow and Stirling areas, thick sandstones occur between two marine limestones, the *Index* and *Calmy* limestones. The sandstones are interpreted to have formed as deltaic channel sands. The *Bishopbriggs* (or *Kenmure*) *Sandstone* was quarried and mined[40] at Bishopbriggs in Huntershill Quarry (Figure 3.9) and at Dullatur Quarry, Kilsyth.[41] At Plean (Blackcraig) Quarry, Kilsyth, the stone was known locally as the *Plean White Freestone*.[42]

At a higher horizon, between the *Huntershill Cement Limestone* and *Lyoncross Coal*, a resistant sandstone occurs both in the Glasgow (where it forms part of the Barrhead Grit) and Stirling areas known as the *Cadger's Loan Sandstone* (or *Rock*). It was worked at Cadger's Loan Quarry which was sometimes referred to as '*Plean*'. However the stone was inferior to that won at Plean (Blackcraig) Quarry and was mainly used for rubble work.[43] The *Giffnock Sandstone* which lies between the *Lyoncross* and *Orchard* limestones[44] and was formerly worked at quarries at Giffnock supplied much stone to Glasgow. Some stone from Giffnock was used in Edinburgh.[45]

Between the *Orchard* and *Calmy* limestones, extensive quarrying took place in the Stirling district in the '*Cowie Rock*' and stone for Edinburgh was wrought at Dunmore and Polmaise quarries.[46] Nearby the original Dunmore Quarry, a new working was opened in 1985 by Scottish Natural Stones Ltd. (Chapter 8).[47]

Passage Formation

The succeeding *Passage Formation* marks a period of increasing deposition of coarse-grained fluvial sediments with periodic marine incursions. Locally, unusually thick coals developed in small isolated rapidly-subsiding basins, for example at Westfield in Fife. Thick sandstones were worked for building stones from an early date at Longannet, Blair and Sands quarries to the north of the Forth near Kincardine.[48] The Old Statistical Account (1794) notes that 'the quarry of Longannat hath been in great reputation, time immemorial. It is a durable stone perfectly white, of a small greek [grain] and takes on a fine smooth polish. The demand for it has been greater than the quarriers have ever been able to supply'.[49]

Coal Measures

Many extensive and workable coals are developed in the *Lower* and *Middle Coal Measures*. Deposition of fluvial channel sands and silts resulted in the formation of a number of thick sandstones. *Lower Coal Measures* sandstones were quarried on an extensive scale in West Lothian, near Fauldhouse and in Midlothian, south of Inveresk and at Bonnyrigg.[50] Sandstone used in Edinburgh was worked at Braehead, West Lothian.[51]

In *Middle Coal Measures* strata, quarries at Auchinlea, Motherwell (Chapters 5 and 8) provided much building stone for Glasgow and some for Edinburgh.[52] The stone lies stratigraphically below a thin development of the *Airdrie Blackband Ironstone*, a resource extensively worked in the Airdrie district from about 1830 until 1875.

Upper Coal Measures sediments were laid down in rivers and deltas. The main rock types are red, white and grey sandstones, siltstones and mudstones. Reddening of the sandstones is believed to have occurred as a result of the movement of oxidizing iron-rich solutions through the strata during Permian times when desert conditions developed. Former quarries in west-central Scotland such as those at Bothwell Park, Uddingston[53] supplied much greyish red and red building stone but there are no documented uses in Edinburgh's buildings.

PERMIAN AND TRIASSIC SANDSTONE ('NEW RED SANDSTONE') OF DUMFRIES & GALLOWAY AND AYRSHIRE

Sandstones of the 'New Red Sandstone' of Permian age, unlike their counterparts in the Carboniferous, developed in desert environments. In south-west Scotland, there is little direct fossil evidence of the age of these rocks which occupy several distinct basins separated from each other by older (Lower Palaeozoic) rocks.[54] Red aeolian sandstones of the *Appleby Group* used in Edinburgh have been quarried over centuries near Dumfries at Locharbriggs, Corncockle, Closeburn and Gatelawbridge and in Ayrshire at Mauchline (Ballochmyle Quarries). Red fluviatile sandstone of the *Sherwood Sandstone Group* is quarried at Corsehill, Annan. About 90 years ago Boyle reviewed the characteristics and uses of the many red sandstone quarries.[55] A recent detailed stratigraphy of the sandstones was published by Brookfield.[56]

Appleby Group
Locharbriggs Sandstone Formation

On the north side of the Dumfries Basin at Locharbriggs up to 25m of the *Locharbriggs Sandstone Formation* is exposed in quarries currently worked by Baird & Stevenson (Quarrymasters) Ltd. (Figure 5.3). Geophysical evidence suggests the strata may attain a otal thickness of up to 1km.[57] The sandstone shows aeolian dune-bedding arranged as wedge-shaped and planar tabular foresets, between 0.5 and 2.0m thick, dipping between 0 and 30° to the south-west. Trackways of reptiles have been found preserved on bedding planes.[58]

Thornhill Sandstone Formation

In the Thornhill Basin, red aeolian, dune-bedded sandstones of the *Thornhill Sandstone Formation*, estimated to be over 200m thick,[59] have been worked over many centuries at he Closeburn[60] and Gatelawbridge[61, 62] quarries near Thornhill. Both sources have supplied Edinburgh with building stone.

Corncockle Sandstone Formation

In the Lochmaben Basin at the intermittently operational Corncockle Quarry, red sandstones of the *Corncockle Sandstone Formation* were formerly noted for the abundance of reptilian footprints found in them (Plate 2).[63] Sedimentary structures include large scale aeolian cross-bedding and tabular foresets which dip up to 40° to the south-west. The vertical face of the quarry exposes up to 30m of strata. As at Locharbriggs, the uniform dip of the cross-lamination indicates that the prevailing winds transported and deposited the sands from the east-north-east.

Mauchline Sandstone Formation

In Ayrshire, the Mauchline Basin contains over 450m of large scale cross-bedded, well-sorted, bright red, fine-grained, aeolian sandstones of the *Mauchline Sandstone*.[64] Building stone was worked in several quarries including Mauchline (Ballochmyle quarries), Barskimming and Failford.[65] The stone was much used in Glasgow. Craig lists stone from Ballochmyle Quarry as having been used in Edinburgh.[66]

Sherwood Sandstone Group
St Bees Sandstone Formation

Early Triassic rocks outcrop in the Annan and Gretna district and form part of the sequence of strata extending southwards into the Carlisle Basin and Vale of Eden.[67] Around Annan they are represented by unfossiliferous water-lain sandstones of the *St*

Bees Sandstone Formation.[68] Stone from this sequence was worked at several quarries including Annanlea,[69] Cove[70] at Kirkpatrick-Fleming (currently operated by Block Stone Ltd) and Corsehill, near Annan.[71, 72] The last-named, recently reopened during 1981 and currently operated by the Onyx Contractors,[73] has supplied much stone to Edinburgh.

PERMIAN AND TRIASSIC SANDSTONE ('NEW RED SANDSTONE') OF MORAY

Strata of the 'New Red Sandstone' in the Elgin district have long been quarried at Cuttieshillock, Clashach, Greenbrae and Spynie. They have yielded much good stone in a variety of colours including white, red and brown. The quarries were famous for yielding fossil reptilian fauna,[74] specimens of which may be seen in the Elgin Museum and National Museum of Scotland. Upper Permian sandstones of Cuttieshillock (Quarry Wood), notable for yielding bones of the *Gordonia* fauna collected during the 19th century, range from 30 to 46m thick and are of variable hardness. Sand grains are typically millet seed-shaped and this together with large scale cross-bedding points to an aeolian origin for the deposits.[75] In 1976, quarries were working this sandstone at Cuttieshillock.[76] However, it is not documented whether stone from this source has in the past been supplied to Edinburgh.

On the Moray coast, the *Sandstones of Hopeman* (considered to be equivalent in age to those of Cuttieshillock) have been used in recent years from Greenbrae and Clashach quarries.[77] Clashach is currently supplying stone to the Stirling Stone Group for several major buildings in Edinburgh (see Chapter 8).

Upper Triassic siliceous sandstones have been worked at Spynie, Elgin.[78] The first specimen of *Leptopleuron* (*Telerpeton*), a small lizard-like reptile was discovered at Spynie in 1851.[79] This discovery raised the question of the true age of the reptile-bearing Elgin sandstones, which hitherto had been regarded as belonging to the Devonian Period.

CARBONIFEROUS SANDSTONE FROM THE SCOTTISH BORDERS AND ENGLAND

Many quarries working Carboniferous sandstones in the Scottish Borders and England (Table 3.2) have supplied top quality building stone for Edinburgh during the ist 100 years. Usage increased as locally available supplies became scarce and as transport, articularly the railway network, developed. In recent years the requirement for matching naterial for repair and for cladding has encouraged a steady trade in stone from England, specially that of Carboniferous age. Durable stone is found at many horizons, most notably in the Lower Carboniferous (Viséan) and *Millstone Grit* (Namurian) sequences of Northumberland, County Durham and Derbyshire. *Coal Measures* (Westphalian) andstones from Yorkshire and Tyne and Wear have also been utilised in the city.

Lower Carboniferous

Strata of Lower Carboniferous age are found over a wide area of the Scottish Borders nd Northern England.[80] As in the Midland Valley of Scotland, Carboniferous sandstones of the Northumberland - Solway Basin were deposited principally in major river systems vhich fed deltas in a subsiding sedimentary basin. Typically, the sandstones suitable for building stones are quartz arenites. Marine and deltaic sedimentation was initially confined to a series of troughs or basins, the principal ones being the Northumberland Trough, the Stainmore Trough and the Craven Basin. Each was partially bounded by iaults, some of which were active during sedimentation. The intervening ground consisted of blocks or massifs named the Cumbrian-Alston Ridge and the Askrigg Block. These were submerged by the sea only in the late Dinantian, and thereafter, with relatively slow subsidence, remained areas of thin Carboniferous sequences.[81] Cyclical sedimentation took place in response to changes of sea level and variation in rates of subsidence and sediment input. Sequences of sedimentary rocks, known as 'Yoredale Cycles', comprise, where complete, a marine limestone, followed by calciferous fossiliferous shale, ferruginous shale with marine fossils, silty shale, sandstone, seat-earth and coal. Each cycle is generally 15 to 30m thick and represents the transition from marine to terrigenous conditions.[82] In the Northumberland Basin the cycles tend to be thinner with a larger terrigenous element representing closer proximity to land.

Cementstone Group

Rocks, roughly equivalent in age and of similar origin to those in the Midland Valley *Ballagan Formation* are found in the *Cementstone Group* of the Scottish Borders. In the Tweed Valley, the strata consist of micaceous mudstone and shale, cementstone and thin sandstone. The lithologies and restricted fauna suggest an estuarine environment in which brackish shallow-water lagoons developed. Thick cross-bedded sandstones are present in the upper part of the group and these have been worked near Greenlaw at Swinton and Whitsome Newton. Both quarries have supplied Edinburgh with stone.[83, 8]

Fell Sandstone Group

The geologically oldest English sandstones used in Edinburgh are found in the *Fell Sandstone Group* of Northumberland. The Group roughly correlates with the middle and upper parts of the *Border Group* of the Scottish Borders but cannot be precisely correlated because of a lack of diagnostic marine fauna.[85] The sandstones, which were deposited as sheet sands in braided rivers,[86] have provided a valuable source of good building stone. In Edinburgh fine representatives can be seen from a number of former quarries, notably Doddington[87, 88] which worked massive, cross-bedded, pink stone. Sandstone for Edinburgh was also worked at Glanton Pike.[89]

In the Langholm district of the Scottish Borders, sandstone of the *Border Group* (equivalent of the *Fell Sandstone* of Northumberland), was formerly quarried at Fairloans, near Hawick.[90]

Scremerston Coal Group

The *Scremerston Coal Group* of north Northumberland roughly correlates with the *Upper Border Group* of North Cumbria where typical sequences comprise limestone – shale - sandstone – seatearth - coal,[91] Sandstones used in Edinburgh have been worked at Cragg near Bellingham,[92] Milknock[93, 94] and Pasturehill[95] quarries.

Lower and Middle Limestone Groups

These groups represent the uppermost part of the Lower Carboniferous (Viséan) up to the base of the *Great Limestone* which is the correlative of the *Hosie Limestones* in the Midland Valley of Scotland. Lithologically, the groups show repeated rhythmic Yoredale cycles: limestone succeeded in turn by calcareous shale, silty shale, sandstone, seat-earth and coal. Many of the sandstones are thick, well-sorted and fine-grained and make good building stones. Edinburgh has been supplied with sandstones from the *Lower Limestone Group* worked at Woodburn.[96] Stone from Blaxter[97] and Darney[98, 99] quarries has been used at various times during the 20th century. Sandstones of the *Middle Limestone Group* have been worked at Cocklaw, Gunnerton, Prudham and Purdovan[100] and also at Denwick.[101] Gunnerton Quarry exposes a 15 to 20m thick coarse-grained, cross-bedded sandstone known as the *Camphill Sandstone*.[102] Medium- to coarse-grained sandstones worked at Cocklaw and Prudham are situated near the top of the Group, below the horizon of the *Great Limestone*.[103]

Millstone Grit

Cyclic sedimentation was maintained throughout Namurian times with the deposition of the *Millstone Grit*. The latter comprises sequences of thin limestones, marine and non-marine shales, sandstones and thin coals. Thick coarse-grained, cross-bedded channel sandstones are also present.[104] Overall, the series represents a transition from the marine-estuarine conditions of the Lower Carboniferous to deltaic and fluvial conditions of the Coal Measures.

Many quarries have exploited the *Millstone Grit* sandstones and those which have supplied Edinburgh include Black Pasture,[105] Catcastle, Dunhouse, Stainton, Stancliffe, Stanton Moor, Stoke Hall, Wattscliffe and Wellfield.[106] All are currently producing stone and may examples of their quarry products may be seen in the city (Chapter 8). Black Pasture quarry exposes some 15m of sandstone with shelly lenticular patches, lying above the *Great Limestone*.[107] At Dunhouse and Stainton, the sandstones lie between the *Upper Fell Top* and *Grindstone Limestones* and consist of up to 12m of pale grey, fine-grained, massive or thick-bedded sandstone. The rock contains 95% free silica, with mica, feldspar and carbonaceous fragments.[108] At Stancliffe, the local *Ashover Grit* comprises 30 to 120m of buff to light grey, massive, fine- to medium-grained sandstone with subordinate bands of siltstone and mudstone.[109] It is said to be excellent for building and decorative purposes. Many quarries including Wellfield worked the *Rough Rock* at Crossland Hill, west of Huddersfield and, in recent years, a light brown, very durable, fine-grained sandstone under the trade name of 'Crosland Hill Hard York Stone'.[110] has been used in Edinburgh. A fine-grained sandstone from Stoke Hall Quarry, Eyam, Derbyshire has also been used in Edinburgh recently.

Coal Measures

Lower and *Middle Coal Measures* crop out over wide areas in Northumberland, Durham, West Cumbria, Lancashire and West Yorkshire. Deltaic and fluvial conditions prevailed in an extensive subsiding gulf. Although cycles of strata are seldom complete, the usual sequence is a marine shale, overlain by non-marine shale, sandstone, seat-earth and coal. Individual cyclothems range from 1 to 30m in thickness. The total thickness of Coal Measures strata varies from 100 to 1200m.[111] Sandstone for Edinburgh has been wrought in *Middle Coal Measures* strata at Heworthburn, Springwell and Woodkirk.[112] The last named is described as a fine-grained, fawn-brown sandstone.[113]

PERMIAN AND TRIASSIC SANDSTONE ('NEW RED SANDSTONE') OF ENGLAND

During late Carboniferous and early Permian times the land was uplifted and erosion produced thick accumulations of wind-blown and fluvial sandstones and siltstones.[114] Red sandstones of Permian and Triassic age crop out west of the Pennines around Carlisle in the Vale of Eden and along a coastal strip south of Whitehaven. In the Vale of Eden, the *Appleby Group* of Permian age comprises *Brockram* (a conglomerate of angular and rounded Carboniferous pebbles in a matrix of red sandstone) overlain by the *Penrith Sandstone Formation* (Table 3.2). The latter (correlated with the desert aeolian red sandstones of the Dumfries & Galloway) is represented by up to 460m of medium- to coarse-grained, generally poorly cemented aeolian sandstones. Cementation with silica is however non-uniform and locally the sandstones are well silicified. They are generally red-brown and dune bedding suggests that they were transported and deposited by winds blowing mainly from the east-south-east.[115] The formation is worked at Lazonby, Penrith[116, 117] and this source has supplied Edinburgh with stone from time to time.

Higher in the sequence the *Cumbrian Coast Group* comprises dull red, evaporitic mudstones, thin sandstones and siltstones containing ripple marks and desiccation cracks. The overlying *St Bees Sandstone Formation* (*Sherwood Sandstone Group*) of early Triassic age (Table 3.2) comprises bright red water-lain, non-marine sandstone with beds of dull red mudstone. In Cumbria, sandstones in this formation are worked intermittently at Bankend Quarry, Bigrigg, Birkham's Quarry, Whitehaven and also at Shawk Quarry, Thursby. Red sandstones from Moat Quarry, north of Longtown, formerly supplied stone for Edinburgh.[118]

REFERENCES

1. Donovan, D.T., *Stratigraphy: an introduction to principles*, New York: John Wiley & Sons, 1966.
2. Lovell, J.P.B., *The British Isles through geological time - a northward drift*. London: Allen and Unwin, 1977.
3. Armstrong, M. and Paterson, I.B., The Lower Old Red Sandstone of the Strathmore Region. *Report of the Institute of Geological Sciences* 70/12, 1970, p.10-11.

4. Mackie, A., Sandstone quarrying in Angus – some thoughts on an old craft. *The Edinburgh Geologist*, 8, 1980, p.14-25.

5. Harry, W.T., The geology of the Dundee District from its quarries. *Quarry Managers' Journal*, 1952, p.491.

6. Miller, Hugh, *The Old Red Sandstone*. Edinburgh: W. P. Nimmo, 1872.

7. Lang, W.H., Contributions to the study of the Old Red Sandstone flora of Scotland. Parts I-VIII, *Transactions of the Royal Society of Edinburgh*, 54-57, 1925-32.

8. Mykura, W., Old Red Sandstone, Chapter 9 in *Geology of Scotland*. G.Y. Craig (editor), 3rd Edition, London: The Geological Society, 1991, p.316.

9. *ibid.*, p.317-318.

10. Donovan, R.N. and Foster, R.J., Subaqueous shrinkage cracks from the Caithness Flagstone Series (Middle Devonian) of north-east Scotland, *Journal of Sedimentary Petrology*, 42, 1972, p.309-317.

11. British Geological Survey, *Thurso: 1:50 000 Geological Sheet 116W, (Solid)*, 1985.

12. Francis, E.H., Carboniferous, Chapter 10 in *Geology of Scotland*. G.Y. Craig (editor), 3rd Edition, London: The Geological Society, 1991, p.347- 392.

13. Cameron, I.B. and Stephenson, D., *The Midland Valley of Scotland*. 3rd Edition, British Regional Geology, British Geological Survey, 1985, p.101-109.

14. *ibid*, p.50.

15. Browne, M.A.E., Dean, M.T., Hall, I.H.S., McAdam, A.D., Monro, S.K. and Chisholm, J.I. A lithostratigraphical framework for the Carboniferous rocks of the Midland Valley. *British Geological Survey Technical Report* WA/96/29, 1996, p.9 –12 and table 1.

16. Mitchell, G.H. and Mykura, W., The geology of the neighbourhood of Edinburgh. 3rd Edition, *Memoir of the Geological Survey of Great Britain*, Sheet 32 (Scotland), 1962, p.28-30.

17. MacGregor, A.G., The mineral resources of the Lothians. *Geological Survey Wartime Pamphlet*, No.45 , 1945, p.16

18. Cameron, I.B. and Stephenson, D., *op. cit.*, p.54-61.

19. Black, G.P., *Arthur's Seat - a history of Edinburgh's volcano*, Edinburgh. Edinburgh: Oliver and Boyd, 1966, p.42.

20. Browne, M.A.E. et al., *op. cit.*, p.21-23 and table 1.

21. Land, D.H. and Cheeney, R.F., *Discovering Edinburgh's volcano: a geological guide to Holyrood Park*. Edinburgh: Edinburgh Geological Society,1996.

22. Mitchell, G.H.and Mykura, W., *op. cit.*, p.53-60.

23. Browne, M.A.E. et al., *op. cit.*, p.21-22.

24. MacGregor, A.G., *op. cit.*, p.17.

25. Mitchell, G.H. and Mykura, W., *op. cit.*, p.53-55.

26. Witham, H., A description of a fossil tree. *Transactions of the Royal Society of Edinburgh*, 12, 1834, p.148.

27. Wood, S.P., Recent discoveries of Carboniferous fishes in Edinburgh. *Scottish Journal of Geology*, 11, 1975, p.251-258.

28. Bennie, J. and Johnston, J.A., Remarks on two transverse sections of Carboniferous wood from Baberton New Quarry, Midlothian. *Proceedings of the Royal Philosophical Society of Edinburgh*, 12, 1894, p.359.

29. MacGregor, A.G., *op. cit.*, p.18.

30. Francis, E.H., The economic geology of the Fife coalfields, Area II, Cowdenbeath and Central Fife. 2nd Edition, *Memoir of the Geological Survey (Scotland)*, 1961, p.14-15, p.134.

31. MacGregor, A.G., *op. cit.*, p.18.

32. Craig, G., Building stones used in Edinburgh: their geological sources, relative durability and other characteristics. *Transactions of the Edinburgh Geological Society*, 6, 1893, p.259-260, 263-264.

33. MacGregor, A.G., *op. cit.*, 1945, p.19.

34. Watson, J., *op. cit.*, p.125, 275.

35. Francis, E.H, *op. cit.*, 1961, p.14-15, p.134.

36. MacGregor, A.G., *op. cit.*, 1945, p.19-22.

37. Craig, George, *op. cit.* , p.267.

38. Francis, E.H, *op. cit.*, 1961, p.14-15, p.134.

39. Lawson, Judith, *The building stones of Glasgow.* Glasgow: Geological Society of Glasgow, 1981, p.8-9, p.20-21, plate 7.

40. Clough, C.T., Hinxman, L.W., Grant Wilson, J.S., Crampton, C.B., Wright, W.B., Bailey, E.B., Anderson, E.M. and Carruthers, R.G., The geology of the Glasgow district, *Memoir of the Geological Survey (Scotland)*, 1911, p.237.

41. Dinham, C.H. and Haldane, D., The economic geology of the Stirling and Clackmannan Coalfield, *Memoir of the Geological Survey (Scotland)*, 1920, p.196-197.

42. *ibid.*

43. *ibid.*

44. Forsyth, I.H., *op. cit.*, 1982, p.8.

45. Craig, George, *op. cit.*, p.266.

46. *ibid*, p.261, 265.

47. Anon. Scottish Revival, *Stone Industries*, 9, November 1985, p.20-21.

48. Dinham, C.H. and Haldane, D., *op. cit.*, p.198-200.

49. Sinclair, Sir J., *The Statistical Account of Scotland*, XI, 1794, p.552.

50. MacGregor, A.G., *op. cit.*, p.20.

51. *ibid.*

52. Clough, C.T., Wilson, J.S.G., Anderson, E.M. and Macgregor, M., The economic geology of the Central Coalfield of Scotland, Area VII, Rutherglen, Hamilton and Wishaw, *Memoir of the Geological Survey (Scotland)*, 1920, p.124-125.

53. *ibid.*

54. Lovell, J.P.B., Permian and Triassic, Chapter 12 in *Geology of Scotland*, edited by G.Y. Craig, 3rd Edition, London: The Geological Society, 1991, p.426-430.

55. Boyle, Robert, The economic and petrographic geology of the New Red Sandstones of the South and West of Scotland, *Transactions of the Geological Society of Glasgow*, 13 , 1909, p.344-384.

56. Brookfield, M E. Revision of the stratigraphy of Permian and supposed Permian rocks of southern Scotland. *Geologischen Rundschau*, Vol. 67, 1978, p. 110-149.

57. Lovell, J.P.B., *op. cit.*, 1991, p.428.

58. McKeever, P.J., A new vertebrate trackway from the Permian of Dumfries and Galloway, *Scottish Journal of Geology*, 30, p. 11-14.

59. McMillan, A.A., A concise account of the geology around New Galloway and Thornhill. *Memoir of the British Geological Survey*, Sheets 9W and 9E (Scotland), in press.

60. Boyle, Robert, *op. cit.*, p.351-354.

61. Craig, George, *op. cit.*, p.269-70.

62. Boyle, Robert, *op. cit.*, p.351-354.

63. Jardine, W., Bart., *The ichnology of Annandale* , Edinburgh, 1853.

64. Lovell, J.P.B., *op. cit.*, 1991, p.427.

65. Boyle, Robert, *op. cit.*, p.357-358.

66. Craig, George, *op. cit.*, p.270.

67. Lovell, J.P.B., *op. cit.*, 1991, p.429-430.

68. Smith, D. B., Brunstrom, R. G. W., Manning, P.I., Simpson, S. and Shotton, F.W., A correlation of Permian rocks in the British Isles. *Special Report of the Geological Society, London*, No.5., 1974.

69. Horne, J. and Gregory, J.W., The Annan Red Sandstone Series of Dumfriesshire, *Transactions of the Geological Society of Glasgow*, 15, 1915, p.374- 386.

70. *ibid.*

71. Craig, George, *op. cit.*, p.270.

72. Boyle, Robert, *op. cit.*, p.347-351.

73. Leary, E. *The building sandstones of the British Isles*, Building Research Establishment, 1986, p.22-23.

74. Benton, M., *The Elgin Reptiles*, Aberdeen People's Press, 1977, 19pp.

75. Peacock, J.D., Berridge, N.G., Harris, A.L. and May, F., The geology of the Elgin district, *Memoir of the Geological Survey of Great Britain*, Sheet 95 (Scotland), 1968, p.57-58.

76. Leary, E., *op. cit.* , p.54.

77. *ibid* , p.20, 35.

78. Peacock, J.D., Berridge, N.G., Harris, A.L. and May, F., *op. cit.*, p.58-63.

79. Mantell, G.A., Description of the Telerpeton elginense, *Quarterly Journal of the Geological Society of London*, 8, 1852, p.100-105, plate 4.

80. Taylor, B.J., Burgess, I.C., Land, D.H., Mills, D.A.C., Smith, D.B. and Warren, P.T., *Northern England*, British Regional Geology, Institute of Geological Sciences, 4th Edition, 1971, p. 6.

81. *ibid* , p.6-7, p.37-40.

82. *ibid*.

83. Watson, J., *British and foreign building stones*, Cambridge University Press, 1911, p.112.

84. Gowans, Sir J., The Memorial Masons' Pillars in *Model Dwelling Houses*, Edinburgh: T. and A. Constable, 1886, p.55-57.

85. Taylor et al., *op. cit.*, 1971, p.44.

86. Hodgson, A.V., Braided river bedforms and related structures in the Fell Sandstone Group (Lower Carboniferous) of North Northumberland, *Proceedings of the Yorkshire Geological Society*, 41, 1978, p.509-532.

87. Craig, George, *op. cit.* , p.270-71.

88. Carruthers, R.G., Dinham, C.H., Burnett, G.A. and Maden, J., The geology of Belford, Holy Island and the Farne Islands, *Memoir of the Geological Survey of Great Britain*, Sheet 4 (England and Wales), 1927, p.161-162.

89. Carruthers, R.G., Burnett, G.A. and Anderson, W. The geology of the Alnwick district, *Memoir of the Geological Survey of Great Britain*, Sheet 6 (England and Wales), 1930, p.109.

90. Lumsden, G.I., Tulloch, W., Howells, M.F. and Davies, A., The geology of the neighbourhood of Langholm, *Memoir of the Geological Survey of Great Britain*, Sheet 11 (Scotland), 1967, p.103.

91. Taylor, B.J., Burgess, I.C., Land, D.H., Mills, D.A.C., Smith, D.B. and Warren, P.T., *op. cit.*, p.51-54.

92. Craig, George, *op. cit.* , p.264-265.

93. Laurie, A.P., *Building materials*, Edinburgh: Oliver and Boyd, 1922, p.30.

94. Frost, D.V. and Holliday, D.W., Geology of the country around Bellingham, *Memoir of the Geological Survey of Great Britain*, Sheet 13 (England and Wales), 1980, p.18.

95. Watson, J., *op. cit.*, p.120.

96. Craig, George, *op. cit.*, p.268.

97. Leary, E., *op. cit.* , p. 12.

98. *Natural Stone Directory*, Stone Industries, 6th Edition, 1985, p.37.

99. Leary, E., *op. cit.* , p.24.

100. Craig, George, *op. cit.*, p.262-64, p.266-68.

101. Cant, M., *Marchmont in Edinburgh*, Edinburgh: John Donald Publishers Ltd., 1984, p.62.

102. Frost, D.V. and Holliday, D.W., *op. cit.*, p.31.

103. *ibid* , p.39, 42, 97, plate 6.

104. Taylor, B.J., Burgess, I.C., Land, D.H., Mills, D.A.C., Smith, D.B. and Warren, P.T., *op. cit.*, p.54-56.

105. Laurie, A.P., *op. cit.* , 1922, p.30.

106. Leary, E., *op. cit.* , p.28, 68, 70, 83-84.

107. Frost, D.V. and Holliday, D.W., *op. cit.*, p.42, plate 8.

108. Mills, D.A.C. and Hull, J.H., Geology of the country around Barnard Castle, *Memoir of the Geological Survey of Great Britain*, Sheet 32 (England and Wales), 1976, p.62-63.

109. Smith, E.G., Rhys, G.H. and Eden, R.A., Geology of the country around Chesterfield, Matlock and Mansfield, *Memoir of the Geological Survey of Great Britain*, Sheet 112 (England and Wales), 1967, p.70, 239 and 271.

110. *Natural Stone Directory*, Stone Industries, 6th Edition, 1985, p.47.

111. Taylor, B.J., Burgess, I.C., Land, D.H., Mills, D.A.C., Smith, D.B. and Warren, P.T., *op. cit.*, p.59.

112. Leary, E., *op. cit.* , p.65, 94-95.

113. *Natural Stone Directory*, Stone Industries, 6th Edition, 1985, p.49.

114. Taylor, B.J., Burgess, I.C., Land, D.H., Mills, D.A.C., Smith, D.B. and Warren, P.T., *op. cit.*, p.76-80.

115. Arthurton, R.S. and Wadge, A.J., Geology of the country around Penrith, *Memoir of the Geological Survey of Great Britain*, Sheet 24 (England and Wales), 1981, p.68-72, 129.

116. *Natural Stone Directory*, Stone Industries, 6th Edition, 1985, p.21.

117. Leary, E., *op. cit.*, p.47.

118. Craig, George, *op. cit.*, p.270.

CHAPTER 4 | TESTS ON BUILDING STONES

"...it is the properties of these common rock-forming minerals, together with their mode of aggregation within a rock, which determines its hardness, durability, porosity, toughness and strength"

EDGAR MORTON, 1926[1]

HISTORY

Attempts to assess the strength and forecast the durability of building stone probably date from its beginnings as a structural material. Quarry owners would have wished to give some quantifiable assurance of the performance of a stone to prospective purchasers. Architects would have needed to satisfy themselves and their clients that a particular stone was suitable for the purpose intended. Unfortunately there appear to be few written records of such tests.

George Smith, architect, writing in 1835, records[2] that Robert Adam 'procured specimens from all the quarries in the neighbourhood and after ascertaining their comparative merits, fixed on Craigleith stone' for **Register House** [128] (c.1776). It would be of interest to know how such an eminent 18th century architect arrived at his decision. The performance of the stone over two centuries and modern tests on Craigleith stone would vindicate Adam's decision on grounds of durability and strength but what were his reasons for rejecting other stones available at that time? Was he solely concerned with strength and long-term appearance? Was influence brought to bear? Presumably the costs of extracting, transporting and working the stone were not significant factors for such a building, but Craigleith quarry was extensively worked during the following hundred years for many less prestigious buildings.

John Rennie (1761-1821) tested the compressive strength of a one-inch cube of Craigleith stone which failed at 12,346 lb; the moisture content, which would have affected the strength, is not stated. The small size of the sample probably reflects the difficulty of applying an intensive known load evenly to a test piece at that time and we are not told if more than one sample was tested. Craigleith stone was also included in the stones considered by the parliamentary inquiry of 1839 to determine a suitable stone for the construction of the new Houses of Parliament.

Hudson Beare of the University of London, who was later to become Professor of Civil Engineering at the University of Edinburgh, undertook what appears to be the first comparative testing of a wide range of British building stones at the end of the 19th century.[3]

The tests he performed gave the compressive stress required to fracture the specimen, specific gravity, mass (or bulk) density of the stone, water absorption and the coefficient of elasticity (Young's modulus). Importantly he described in considerable detail how the samples were obtained and the tests performed. The latter is important because variations in test methods can cause significant variations in results. Beare also subjected some of the specimens to a freezing test for which he had to rely upon natural conditions; freezing previously soaked specimens by placing them out of doors overnight and thawing them indoors during the day. The test was terminated by a thaw.

Beare obtained his samples for testing by the simple expedient of inviting quarry owners to submit three specimens of stone in the form of two and one quarter inch cubes. We may presume that these were very likely selected samples of the best stone that the quarry could produce and therefore not representative samples. Beare may have restricted the number of specimens from each quarry to keep the tests to a manageable number, bearing in mind the time required to perform the tests. It is likely that he recognised the limitations of testing such a small number of specimens from each quarry but he was seeking comparative values and probably did not expect his results to be quoted unquestioningly and out of context in the years that followed.

Quite apart from the difficulty of obtaining representative values from three small samples of extensive masses of heterogeneous material, the tests must have required careful sequencing to ensure that any one test did not affect a property which was to be tested thereafter using the same specimen. The specimen size was derived by estimating the size of the strongest stone which could be crushed in the 100,000 lb testing machine of University College.

The compression tests performed by Rennie and Beare were on cubes of stone. Nowadays, compression tests are performed on cylindrical columns of stone; normally with a height to diameter ratio of 2.5:1. Such a column would fail at a lower applied load than a cube of identical material. Furthermore, the method of transmitting the load to the test specimen, the characteristics of end plates and any packing pieces, the characteristics of the test machine and the rate at which the load is applied affect results. Therefore a comparison of strength based on compression test results is likely to be misleading.

CURRENT METHODS OF TESTING

One of the consequences of the First World War was the acceleration of the decline in the use of dressed stone for building. The development of standard tests on stone was driven by the increasing use of crushed stone for aggregates and the needs of engineers to assess the in-situ strength of rock in mining, tunnelling and excavations. Testing of facing stone for the renovation and construction of buildings continued in research establishments and standard procedures have emerged which have been adopted, with some variants, prior to the publication of British Standards and equivalent internationally accepted standards. Differences in procedures can give different results so a knowledge of the test procedure used is desirable if comparisons are to be made.

However, it is important to bear in mind that, whilst tests can be standardised, stone is a naturally variable material and the measurable characteristics of suitable stones for building fall within wide ranges of values compared with those for products manufactured to satisfy a British Standard. Test results should be regarded as indicative rather than absolute values of a stone's properties. Indeed, there may be considerable acceptable variations within a quarry, giving a choice of compatible stone for differing applications.

An important aspect of Beare's work was that it provided a comparison of the majority of building stones available at that time. His results are reported in full in his paper 'Building Stones of Great Britain – their crushing strength and other properties'.[4] The data tabulated in this book (Appendix 5) were compiled to provide a similar modern comparison of the properties of sandstones used historically and currently in Edinburgh. Most of the data in this edition are based on tests undertaken at Napier University. They have been supplemented by data made available by the Building Research Establishment and the Edinburgh New Town Conservation Committee and their contributions are gratefully acknowledged. Sufficient tests have been undertaken to show that results from these three sources are compatible within the natural variation of the sandstones tested.

TESTS USED AS INDICATORS OF DURABILITY
Porosity

The majority of stones used for building are sedimentary rocks and, in Edinburgh, sandstones predominate. These stones are composed of grains of sand bound together by natural cements. The spaces between the particles are not completely filled with cement, leaving pore spaces which are normally assumed to be interconnecting. The porosity of a stone is defined as the ratio of the volume of the pore space to the total volume of the stone. The pores vary in size and shape, depending upon the size distribution of the particles and the degree of cementation.

Therefore two stones, having the same porosity, could have very different pore structures; at the simplest, one could contain relatively few but large pores whilst the other contained many much smaller pores. The two stones would have very different absorption characteristics. It follows therefore that a knowledge of the porosity alone is insufficient and the pore size and shape distribution should also be known. Unfortunately this cannot be measured directly and consequently tests have been devised to give indirect measures of these characteristics.

Water Absorption

The absorption of a stone is defined as the ratio of the volume of water absorbed, when the stone is immersed at atmospheric pressure, to the volume of the stone. It is an indication of the readiness of the stone to absorb water when exposed to the elements. The sample of stone is dried in an oven at between 101°C and 105°C, just hot enough to remove any moisture contained in the pores. The sample is weighed and immersed in water for 24 hours, at the end of which time the surface moisture is removed with a damp cloth and the sample weighed again. The difference in weight gives the mass, and hence the volume, of water absorbed. The ratio of the volume of water absorbed to the volume of the sample is the water absorption and is expressed as a percentage.

In the past this value was sometimes misleadingly quoted as the porosity whereas the total pore space is only partially filled with water during this test.

Quoted values for both absorption and porosity have sometimes been calculated as the ratio of the mass of water absorbed to the mass of the dry sample of stone, expressed as a percentage. Values calculated thus are dependent upon the mass density of the stone, itself a function of the porosity and the constituent minerals. The resulting 'porosity' and 'absorption' values are misleadingly low and are of the order of 40% of those calculated by volume; the relative density of porous rocks being about 2.0 to 2.6 that of water.

The porosity is obtained by filling the pores with a non-reactive fluid. The latter is achieved usually by filling the pores with distilled water under vacuum. This method depends upon the assumption that the pores are interconnected and that all can be filled by a liquid from the outside of the sample. This is usually the case with building sandstones but strictly speaking this yields the 'apparent porosity'. The 'true porosity' can be derived by calculation from the mass density of the solid material and the bulk density of the stone.

The relationship between the volume of fluid absorbed and the vacuum applied gives an indication of the pore-size distribution.

Saturation Coefficient

A simplified approach is to calculate the 'Saturation Coefficient',[5] the ratio of water absorption to porosity. A stone with predominantly small pores draws water in by capillary action at atmospheric pressure so that the 'water absorption' approximates to the true 'porosity', giving a high value for the saturation coefficient. Such a stone is supposed to be less durable when exposed to atmospheric conditions than a stone containing a greater proportion of large pores which would have a relatively low saturation coefficient. The latter stone would have a greater volume of free pore space in which crystals of ice or pollutants could form without creating internal stresses.

However, taken on its own, saturation coefficient is not a reliable guide to durability. This measure of purely physical characteristics does not take into account the effects of mineral constituents which may affect durability adversely, for example, the characteristic of some clays to swell over a period of time when exposed on the face of a building. Also a stone of proven durability, like Craigleith, can have a relatively high saturation coefficient combined with a very low porosity; the latter factor in this example being indicative of the high degree of cementation which contributes to the strength of a stone.

Acid immersion test

Stones containing calcium carbonate, i.e. limestones and some sandstones are susceptible to attack from the weak acid present in rainfall, particularly in urban areas. A dry sample of the stone is immersed in a 20% solution of sulphuric acid for ten days and the effects recorded.

Sodium Sulphate Crystallisation test

In the Sodium Sulphate Crystallisation test,[6] the sample is repeatedly soaked in a solution of sodium sulphate and oven-dried in a humid atmosphere, inducing rapid crystal growth within the pores. A saturated solution may be used for sandstones whereas a 14% solution provides an adequate test for limestones. The test is continued to disintegration or to 15 complete cycles, whichever is the less, and the effects recorded.

The test has been criticised because it does not have a sound theoretical basis. Nevertheless, it provides the most practical means available of testing the potential durability of building stones but it is time-consuming and therefore slow and expensive to undertake.

A second criticism is that stones, which have proved satisfactory in practice, do not survive more than half the cycles and there is not a clear and simple distinction between the satisfactory and the unsatisfactory. Stones that have proved satisfactory in use may appear well down the range of possible values. Reference to Appendix 5 shows the validity of this criticism. The nature of the formation of stone is such that it grades continuously from the weak to the durable and tests reflect this gradation. The saturated sulphate solution provides a particularly severe test and an unsuitable facing stone is likely to show its weaknesses at a very early stage in the test, at as few as two or three cycles. Examples of such unsatisfactory stones have not been identified in use in Edinburgh and therefore do not appear in the data for comparison.

THE MECHANICAL PROPERTIES OF STONE
Strength tests

The property most usually quoted historically is that of compressive strength. Compressive in this context is the means of applying the load by compression along one axis, between the platens of a testing machine; the uniaxial or unconfined compression test. Brittle rocks are not easily compressed and the specimen fails primarily due to shear and, possibly, tensile stresses induced by the application of the compressive load. The maximum load and the nature of the failure depend upon the shape of the specimen and the characteristics of the testing machine. The compression test[7] requires careful specimen preparation, a powerful testing-machine and is not suitable for all types of rock.

A strength test that has found favour since 1970 is the point-load test.[8, 9] A compressive load is applied through two conical loading points until the specimen splits, failing due to the tensile stress developed perpendicularly to the axis of the applied load. The test may be used in the field because the specimens require only rough shaping with a hammer and the relatively small load required can be applied with the aid of a hand-operated jack. The ease with which specimens can be prepared and tested and the consistency of results means that a high degree of reliability can be placed on the strength index obtained.

Uniaxial or Unconfined Compression test

Nowadays this test is usually performed on cylindrical specimens, using standard diamond drill cores. It is important that the diameter is constant and that the ends are parallel to one another and perpendicular to the axis of the cylinder. This is more difficult to achieve in some rocks than others. The specimen is immersed in water for 24 hours prior to the test. The length, L and diameter, D, are measured. The specimen is placed between the parallel flat platens of the testing machine and compressed until failure occurs, the maximum load, P, being recorded. The compressive strength is recorded as the load at failure divided by the cross-sectional area of the specimen.[10] This method of testing permits the deformation of the specimen to be measured and the modulus of elasticity, E, to be derived.

The Point-Load test

The specimen of rock is compressed between two hardened steel points until it splits, the failure being predominantly due to tensile stress induced perpendicularly to the plane of loading. The points are hardened steel cones, rounded to a radius of 5mm at their tips. The points may be fitted to a laboratory testing machine or used in a light portable rig, using a hand-operated hydraulic jack to apply the load. Specimens may be pieces of drill core or fragments of rock about 50mm in diameter. The length is normally between one and two times the diameter. Correction factors have been developed for application to results obtained on specimens which are above or below the recommended sizes. The point-load strength index is expressed as P/D^2 where P is the load at failure in MN (MegaNewtons) and D is the diameter of the specimen in metres. Some workers have shown a relationship between the point-load index and compressive strength but, in general, insufficient results are available to make other than a generalised relationship.

Hardness

The hardness[11] may be tested in the field, using a Schmidt rebound hammer or in the laboratory, where alternatively a scleroscope may be used. Both tests give results on arbitrary scales which have un-established relationships with the strength and ease of working of the stone.

REFERENCES

1. Morton, E., The microscopic determination of the strength and durability of building stones. *Engineering*, 24 Sept 1926.

2. Smith, G., Account of the quarries of sandstone in the Edinburgh and Glasgow districts and of the principal slate quarries in Scotland, *Prize Essays and Transactions of the Highland and Agricultural Society of Scotland*, (New Series), 4, 1835, p.81-97.

3. Beare, T.H., Building stones of Great Britain - their crushing strength and other properties, *Proceedings of the Institution of Civil Engineers*, CVII, 1891, p.341-369.

4. *ibid.*

5. Honeyborne, D.B. and Harris, P.B., The structure of porous building stone and its relation to weathering behaviour, *Proceedings of the Symposium of the Colston Research Society*, University of Bristol, 10, 1958, p.343.

6. Building Research Establishment, *The selection of natural building stone*, Digest 269, 1983.

7. Brown, E.T. (editor), *Rock characterisation, testing and monitoring; ISRM Suggested Methods*, Pergamon Press, 1981.

8. Broch, E. and Franklin, J.A., The point-load strength test, *International Journal of Rock Mechanics and Mining Sciences*, 9, 1972, p.669-697.

9. Bienawski, Z.T., The point-load test in geotechnical practice, *Engineering Geology*, 9, 1975, p.1-11.

10. Beare, T.H., *op.cit.*, 1891.

11. Brown, E.T. (editor), *op. cit.*, 1981.

Note. Appendix 5 (page 202) gives a summary of the properties of building stones used in Edinburgh.

CHAPTER 5 | QUARRYING METHODS

"There is no part of Scotland where the working of freestone is better understood or executed than in Edinburgh"

GEORGE SMITH, 1835.[1]

WORKING OF THE STONE

The ability of the quarryman to appreciate and exploit the geological character of stone is of prime importance to its successful use in buildings. As shown in Chapter 2 sandstones from different quarries differ in quality in their colour, texture, hardness and ability to resist weathering. The qualities of a stone may not be obvious until it has been exposed to the weather in a building for several years. Differential weathering is often seen in a quarry face particularly if the quarry is used only intermittently and the experienced quarryman uses a knowledge of weathering characteristics to predict how the stone will stand in a building. Minute fissures (vents or drys) or 'sand holes' may only show when the stone is used in a building. Almost as troublesome as fissures are the nodules of hard material 'white' or 'bastard whin' found, for example, in the Redhall quarries, Edinburgh and the beds of whin which had to be blasted in Binny Quarry, West Lothian.[2]

The equipment and methods used to work sandstone have changed little over the centuries. Examples of some of the manual tools are shown in Figure 5.1. A photograph of quarrymen at work in Corncockle Quarry, taken in the 1930s (Figure 5.2), illustrates the use hammers and wedges. Mattocks, hoes, shovels, rakes and spades were for uncovering the stone, removing the overburden or 'tirr' as it was called. Hammers of various shapes and weights were used to shape the stone or to drive in the drills. Crowbars or picks were often employed to lever the stone off the bed so that it could be lifted with a crane. It is these simple tools which are most often mentioned in early records of the Masters of Works and the Town Council. Payment is recorded for the sharpening of three dozen picks at Ravelston and Salisbury quarries (July 1530).[3] Old picks and mattocks were made into a new mattock and six new wedges in October 1531.[4] During the work at Newhaven in April-May 1556 iron was bought for picks and mattocks and wood for mattock shafts. Repairs were also carried out on heavy hammers, picks and crow bars.[5] The main modern development has been in the use of mechanical equipment for moving stone. From the earliest times cranes were used, first operated by muscle-power (human or horse) then powered by steam, diesel and electricity (Figure 5.3). Some old Edinburgh quarries still have the stone seats for steam cranes (e.g. Ravelston Black and Barnton Park). Mechanical methods of stripping the overburden, either glacial drift or useless strata, were introduced during this century.

When there is no natural jointing to yield a manageable lump of stone, it has to be split. For small blocks of stone splitting is effected by hammering in wedges. The plug

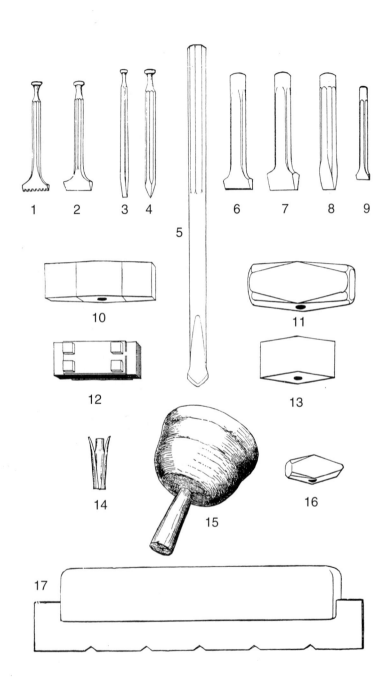

Figure 5.1 Hand implements used in stone working

Adapted from Merrill, G P. Stones for Building and Decoration. (1910, New York: John Wiley & Sons)
1.   Tooth chisel used on soft stone
2.   Chisel or drove
3 & 9. Chisel used on soft stone and driven with wooden mallet
4.   Point, cutting end in form of a pyramidal point
5.   Hand drill or jumper used for making holes for 'plug & feather' splitting
6& 7.   Point for use on hard stone
8.   Splitting chisel for splitting and cutting of hard stone such as granite
10.   Face hammer, square-faced, for roughly shaping blocks
11.   Sledge or striking hammer used in driving large wedges for splitting stone
12.   Patent or bush hammer with deeply grooved faces
13.   Ax or pean hammer with two opposite cutting edges
14.   Wedge (plug) and feather used in the process of splitting (up to 8cm long); long wedges (30cm) for split-
        ting off large blocks
15.   Mallet, wooden, cylindrical head, used in cutting of soft stone
16.   Hand hammer, smooth-faced, for hand-drilling, pointing and chiselling hard rocks
17.   Grub saw for cutting stone by hand

and feathers method is used for larger pieces. In the latter method a row of shallow vertical holes is drilled along the line of the intended split at intervals, the distance of which depends on the hardness of the stone. Often, an interval of about 23cm is chosen. Split iron rods (feathers) are dropped into the holes and iron wedges (plugs) are driven in. This produces a clean break a few metres deep. The same plugs and feathers are further used to shape the block so produced.[6] Another method is to make a 5 to 8mm deep groove along the desired fracture within which a row of holes for the feathers can be drilled. The grooves and holes can be cut with a hammer and chisel but for deeper holes a pneumatic drill is used. When the great Edinburgh quarries were in operation holes were drilled with a jumper, a bar of iron, steel-tipped and forged into a chisel-shaped wedge. Sometimes this bar was used as a percussion drill, being driven into the sandstone by one man, under its own weight. Alternatively the drill was struck with an iron headed hammer, known as a mash. Used in this way, two or three men were required, one sitting holding the jumper vertically between his knees, and rotating it slightly between strokes which were delivered by one or two hammer men. In the first method, also known as 'churn drilling', when a 30 cm hole had been made, water was usually poured into the borehole and a leather collar or washer made of straw placed on the drilling rod to stop the water spilling out. Muddy material would be removed from the borehole with a scraper which consisted of a thin iron rod with a disc at the end. [7]

When the quarry shows strong vertical joints (as in many Scottish quarries) wedges are hammered in horizontally to cleave a suitably sized block from the face enough to allow the attachment of a chain. A crane at the quarryhead can then be used to pull the block free.[8] Sometimes a small charge of black powder is used to split a stone. Whatever the nature of the stone it is essential that it be carefully handled both during and after quarrying. Large charges of explosive are rarely used when regularly shaped building stone is required. The use of excessive explosive produces minute cracks in the rock into which water may enter to accelerate the decay of the stone. Even a dropped or knocked stone may develop scaling at the site of the shock when the stone is exposed to weathering. In their hey-day, most of Edinburgh's sandstone quarries used little blasting powder. For example, in 1835 Smith noted[9] that at Craigleith 'On an average 25 pounds will cover the annual use of gunpowder'. When powder was used it was generally to bring down stone to be used for rubble work. A tool called a reamer is used to cut a groove down each side of a previously drilled shot hole in the direction of the desired break and the elongated hole is then charged and fired. Coarse-grained black powder is preferred to other blasting agents (e.g. dynamite) since it acts more slowly and less shattering is produced.[10] Generally the use of gunpowder was not popular in sandstone quarries.

FIGURE 5.2 Corncockle Quarry, Lochmaben
The close up shows use of the chisel wedge method to split the stone to the required dimensions. BGS Photograph C3606 (1937). Reproduced by permission of the Director, British Geological Survey. © NERC. All rights reserved.

FIGURE 5.3 Locharbriggs Quarry, Dumfries

This photograph shows a general view of the working face. The sandstone was worked 'against the dip'. Situated at the top of the quarry is a regiment of modern electrically powered cranes with steel lattice jibs capable of lifting up to 150 cubic feet of stone. Blocks 12' x 6' on their natural bed could be lifted. In the foreground a block of stone is ready to be raised to the surface for cutting and dressing. An LMS wagon can just be discerned in the background, a reminder that stone was transported by railway directly from the quarry. BGS Photograph C3598 (1937). Reproduced by permission of the Director, British Geological Survey. © NERC. All rights reserved.

quarries. James Gowans introduced a new technique which was said to be an improvement on the traditional wedging method at his quarry at Redhall in about 1850. A row of 7.5 to 10cm diameter holes of considerable depth was drilled at a suitable distance from the quarry face. These were then charged with gunpowder and fired simultaneously by an electric battery. The method produced a large amount of stone cheaply.[11] An alternative method of blasting used more recently in some Scottish quarries (e.g. Locharbriggs and the new Dunmore quarries) uses the rapid conversion of liquid carbon dioxide into a gas to produce the relatively slow heaving action necessary to move the sandstone without shattering it. This method is known as Cardox blasting.[12]

Some quarries were worked by channelling which involved cutting a groove or channel 6m long and 3m deep along the side and back of the piece of stone which was to be extracted. Channelling was a suitable method in quarries where the beds dipped at a shallow angle. Long ago channelling was done with picks but later a specially adapted drill was able to cut a deep groove in any direction using a set of bits working by percussion. Channelling using the Ingersoll-Sargeant channelling machine was first introduced into Scotland by the owners of North Auchinlea Quarry, Motherwell and was in use by 1911.[13] Once the channel was made the block could be split off the bed with wedges and crowbars.[14]

Most sandstone in Scotland has been worked in open quarries. The size of stone block which the quarry can produce depends on the lifting power of available cranes. The Locharbriggs crane lifts blocks from depths of between 9 and 36m. Occasionally stone was found at a depth where the removal of overburden proved uneconomic. In some cases the stone was considered to be valuable enough to be mined by pillar and stall methods, as at the Braidbar quarries, Giffnock where galleries about 9m high by 18m wide were opened. At Huntershill Quarry, Bishopbriggs, where galleries 15m high were

Figure 5.4 Corsehill Quarry, Annan
In the dressing yard masons are shown at work using mells (wooden mallets) and chisels on the stone. Note that many of the blocks were sawn and that the small holes cut in the faces were used for gripping the block with dogs and chain sling (see block in the foreground).
BGS Photograph C3603 (1937). Reproduced by permission of the Director, British Geological Survey. © NERC. All rights reserved.

opened (Figure 3.9), sandstone was mined for more than fifty years until a serious roof fall killed five men at the beginning of this century. [15] Sandstone was mined until more recently at Dalachy near Burntisland in Fife.

It has been estimated that more than three tonnes of stone have to be quarried to produce one tonne of principal stone products.[16] The rest (75-80%) is sorted for sale as rubble, roadstone or shivers, or rejected as spoil. Rubble was used extensively during the 19th century for the back walls, gables and internal walls of tenements and other buildings (see also Chapter 6). Some quarries (e.g. Hailes) became known for the high quality of the rubble produced. Today there is little demand for rubble in modern building work although ornamental rubble walls are still built. The principal stone lifted from the quarry is often 'blocked' (cut to roughly rectangular shape) for immediate sale or transported to dressing sheds.

It is in the finishing of building stone that the main cost lies. Until quite recently the roughly shaped stone which left the quarry was hand-dressed (Figure 5.4). Sometimes it was left rough on the exposed surface (rock-faced) or droved, tooled or polished with special equipment.

Stone dressing is now mostly done by machines. The irregular lump from the quarry is first cut into slabs with a frame saw. This saw has a rectangular horizontal frame suspended by rods holding several parallel steel blades from 76-150mm (3-6″) deep, 5mm (3/16″) thick and 2 - 4.5m (6-15 feet) long. These blades are at adjustable distances from each other and are driven backwards and forwards to cut the stone. Water, together with an abrasive, which may be sand, steel shot or carborundum to help the cutting process, is sprayed over the cuts. In order to cut the remaining faces on the stone the slabs may then be clamped to a moving table which feeds them against one or two revolving circular saw blades, the tips of which may have small diamonds set into their edges. More accurate, though slower cutting work is done with a carborundum rimmed steel blade. Water has to be fed on to the circular blades to keep them cool. If a very fine finish is required, relatively expensive wire sawing methods are employed. Wire saws (single or multi-wire) are used with water and an abrasive to cut sandstone which is mounted on a bogey. Any marks made by the cutting process can be removed by placing the stone on a rotating circular steel table. The abrasive action of carborundum, sand and water between the fixed stone and the rotating table smoothes the stone.[17] Computer controlled profiling machines have revolutionised the 'running' of moulding in recent years.

Hand finishing, now aided by power tools such as a pneumatic hammer or pointed pick or punch, is still used to remove final rough edges or to texture the stone.

Compressed air and abrasives are also used for texturing. Hand work on a bench is still very important in the repair and replacement of carved stone in old buildings where the work can only be partly done mechanically.[18]

ORGANISATION OF WORK

Accounts of early building in Scotland provide little information about the organisation of quarrying. Certainly detail is much scarcer than in English documents. Some information comes from the building accounts for larger works like Holyrood Palace, Edinburgh Castle and Parliament House. From the 16th century onwards the Town Council records are helpful. Almost certainly the first large-scale widespread quarrying in Scotland took place in Roman times when the Roman Army had its specialist quadratarii or stone cutters. More notable examples of Roman masonry above the ground north of Hadrian's Wall include Cramond Fort and Bearsden Bathhouse. In mediaeval times, abbeys and castles were very often built from locally quarried stone. An example is **Craigmillar Castle** which must have required large supplies of local stone. In the few surviving early accounts little is said about transport of stone which suggests that many Scottish buildings used local stone. However, even in 16th century Edinburgh, when major work was being undertaken at Holyrood Palace stone was brought from as far away as Cramond, Barnbougle and Queensferry and even from Culross in Fife. Quarries near these coastal villages supplied stone which was transported by ship to Leith and thence to **Holyrood Palace** [146] or **Edinburgh Castle** [9]. Transport costs could be a significant factor in the price of Edinburgh building stones. The cost of carting or sledging stone from the quarry to the building site could be almost as much as the cost of winning the stone at the quarry face (e.g. Ravelston, Chapter 7).

In the early days of quarrying in Edinburgh the demand was mainly for rubble which was used in the Old Town tenements. These comparatively small stones could be supplied from local quarries where the depth of working was not great (e.g. Bruntsfield, Quarry Holes and Society). In the 17th century prestigious buildings in the Old Town, such as Heriot's Hospital (**George Heriot's School**) [33]and **Parliament House** [21] and the great undertakings of the New Town in the late 18th century, such as **Register House** [128] and the **Old College** of the **University of Edinburgh** [28], demanded stone of consistent size, colour, durability and quantity which the small-scale workings could not supply. It was then that the great quarries of Craigleith and Ravelston came into full production as the thickness of the beds in these quarries was sufficiently great to provide the large ashlar blocks which these buildings demanded as well as abundant rubble for wall cores. Indeed it was said that Craigleith quarry could produce stone of any size providing there was powerful enough machinery to move it.[19]

Quarries were often worked by groups of men ('marrows'). For example, 24 workmen and 7 quarriers were paid for a week's work in May 1529 but they worked four quarries during the course of the week, namely Salisbury, Ravelston, Leith Hill and a quarry at Culross.[20] Sometimes the work involved the clearing ('redding') of the quarry as well as 'putting down' the stones ready for use at Holyrood. These men probably worked in small groups to enable the quarry face to be developed in a series of short lengths, each of which was in advance of the next. The vertical face was probably divided into a series of terraces, as at Clashach, Corsehill and Locharbriggs today, so that the whole face was carried back uniformly.[21] The number of men working at a quarry at any time depended on the demand for stone for a particular building and the number employed could fluctuate according to the season. Most, though not all, work was carried on in the summer months and the shorter winter day was reflected in a reduced wage for quarriers as it was for masons.

The length of working day for quarriers was probably the same as that for masons. In Edinburgh during summer-time in the early 16th century quarriers worked from 5 am to 7 pm. A two hour break was taken at midday and two short breaks observed of half-an-hour for breakfast ('disjune')and, except in the depths of winter, another half-hour afternoon break for 'nunshankis'. In winter they worked from dawn to 11.30 am then from 1 pm till dusk. By the 18th century summer hours had been reduced to 6 am to 7 pm with one hour for breakfast and another for lunch.[22] Pay day was Saturday.[23]

THE WORKMEN

In Scotland there was less distinction between the different types of stone workers than in England. The work of winning stone was undertaken by men variously described as quarriers or workmen. It seems that those described as quarriers were the skilled men with whom the masters of works made the contracts to quarry specified amounts of stone. Workmen did the labouring. Often the men who quarried the stone also did some of the shaping. Sometimes quarriers may have moved up the social scale to become masons who were members of a trade. (e.g. John Merlion, a quarrier at Barnbougle in July 1535 was described as a mason working at the kitchen of Holyrood Palace in August 1538).[24] This was certainly the case with one of the few stone cutters to achieve fame, Hugh Miller, who began his working life as a quarryman in February

1820 in the Cromarty quarries. 'It was the necessity which made me a quarrier that taught me to be a geologist.' [25] His first job as a quarryman was to 'red up' the quarry, using a shovel to move loose rocks which obscured the working face. This done, 'Picks and wedges, and levers, were applied by my brother-workmen; and, simple and rude as I had been accustomed to regard these implements, I found much to learn in the way of using them.' When these simple methods failed gunpowder was used. 'We had a few capital shots: the fragments flew in every direction.'[26] Miller provides[27] a glimpse of an aspect of the skilled quarrier and mason's life which must have applied throughout many parts of Scotland for hundreds of years. Shortage of work often led to these men travelling around the country to where major building work was being undertaken. In Miller's case it was to Cononside then later to Edinburgh where work on Niddrie House took place during the building boom of the mid-1820s. In these travels Miller experienced the hard life of the barrack, or workman's lodging.

Most quarrymen were probably illiterate so it is hardly surprising that we have few accounts of what it was like to work in a quarry when stone was won by human muscle. However, in addition to the writings of Hugh Miller, there is the autobiography of Alexander Somerville, born in East Lothian in 1811. In the course of a very varied life he spent some time in 1830 as a labourer in the Pan Doocot (Dovecot) quarry in East Lothian. Here, stone was quarried for the new Cove Harbour then being built 3km away. The labourers cut the stone from the quarry face and the masons then hewed the stone blocks into shape. According to Somerville the masons looked down on their assistants, who did not have a trade, and treated them very badly to the extent of striking them at small provocation.[28]

Life for stone workers was never very healthy as the comments about respiratory problems at Craigleith Quarry make clear (Chapter 7). It was probably slightly healthier for the quarriers than the masons as the former worked in the open air while the latter, working in groups as at Holyrood in February 1530,[29] dressed stone in sheds or lodges in which much dust was created.[30]

REFERENCES

1. Smith, G., Account of the quarries of sandstone in the Edinburgh and Glasgow districts, and of the principal slate quarries in Scotland, *Prize Essays and Transactions of the Highland and Agricultural Society of Scotland*, (New Series), 4, 1835, p.82.

2. *ibid.*, p.88.

3. Paton, H.M. (editor) *Accounts of the Masters of Works for building and repairing Royal Palaces and Castles*, (1529-1615), 1, H.M.S.O., 1957, p.48.

4. Smith, G., *op. cit.*, 1835, p.59.

5. *Extracts from the Records of the Burgh of Edinburgh* (1528-1557), 1938, p.324-325.

6. Ashurst, J. and Dimes, F.G., *Stone in building: its use and potential today*, London: The Architectural Press, 1977, p.25.

7. *Minutes of Evidence taken before the Royal Commission on Metalliferous Mines and Quarries*, 2, H.M.S.O., 1914.

8. Greenwell, A. and Elsden, J.V., *Practical stone quarrying. A manual for managers, inspectors and owners of quarries and for students*, London: Crosby, Lockwood and Co., 1913, p.220-221.

9. Smith, G., *op. cit.*, 1835, p.84.

10. Greenwell, A. and Elsden, J.V., *op. cit*, 1913, p. 486-87.

11. Bremner, D., *The industries of Scotland*, Adam and Charles Black, 1869, p.412.

12. McAdam, R., and Westwater, R., *Mining explosives*, Edinburgh: Oliver and Boyd, 1958, p.86-87.

13. Clough, C.T., Wilson, J.S.G., Anderson, E.M. and Macgregor, M., The economic geology of the Central Coalfield of Scotland, Area VII, Rutherglen, Hamilton and Wishaw, *Memoir of the Geological Survey (Scotland)*, 1920, p.124.

14. Greenwell, A., and Elsden, J.V., *op. cit.*, 1913, p.250.

15. *ibid*, p.169, 286.

16. Broughton, H.F., Illingworth, J.R., and Rice, G.G., Survey of building in sandstone in Scotland, *National Building Studies Special Report* No. 20, D.S.I.R. 1953, p.15.

17. McKay, W.B., *Building construction*, 1, London: Longmans, Green and Co., 1948, p.36.

18. Ashurst, J., and Dimes, F.G., *op.cit.*, 1977, p.30-32.

19. Smith, G., *op. cit.*, 1835, p.82.

20. Paton, H.M. (editor) *op.cit.*, 1957, p.2.

21. Greenwell, A., and Elsden, J.V., *op.cit.*, 1913, p.111.

22. Knoop, D., and Jones, G.P. *The Scottish mason and the mason word*, Manchester: Manchester University Press 1939, p.40-41.

23. Paton, H.M. (editor) *op.cit.*, 1957, p.xlvi. (Introduction).

24. *ibid*, p.136, p.223.

25. Miller, H., *My schools and schoolmasters*, Edinburgh: W.P. Nimmo, Hay and Mitchell, 1907, p.55.

26. Miller, H., *The Old Red Sandstone*, Edinburgh: W.P. Nimmo, 1877, p.36.

27. Miller, H., *op.cit.*, 1907, chapters 9, 10 and 14.

28. Somerville, A. *The autobiography of a working man*, London: MacGibbon & Kee, 1967 (first published 1848), p.96.

29. Paton, H.M. (editor), *op.cit.* , 1957, p.17.

30. *Minutes of Evidence taken before the Royal Commission on Metalliferous Mines and Quarries*, 2, H.M.S.O., 1914.

CHAPTER 6 | THE USE AND AVAILABILITY OF SANDSTONE IN EDINBURGH

"Ideal stone is durable, strong and of a colour which would best bring out the architectural features of his [the architect's] design, and harmonise with the locality and surroundings"

JAMES GOWANS, 1883[1]

The buildings of Edinburgh provide an open-air museum of quarry products, walling methods and stone finishes. Examples of the use of sandstone from famous quarries, many long since abandoned and filled in, can be observed. The weathering characteristics of stones subjected to many years of exposure to the atmosphere of 'Auld Reekie', can be compared and contrasted. Although exotic stone of igneous and metamorphic origin from all over the world can be observed as cladding or 'geological wallpaper'[2] on shop fronts, the emphasis in this account is placed on sandstone, both its traditional, structural uses and as cladding.

METHODS OF WALLING

Sandstone has been built into structures in a variety of ways. When stones have little or no work done on them after they come from the quarry, they are described as rubble. The broken pieces of stone, often of varying shape and size may be built as random rubble walls as in the **Flodden Wall** at the **Vennel** [32] (Figure 6.1a). Early tenements were also rubble-built and **No. 7 West Nicolson Street** is a fine late 18th century example (Figure 6.1b). An example of a modern rubble wall may be seen on the south side of Holyrood Park Road near the **Commonwealth Pool**. Rubble walls are relatively cheap to construct and may be built either uncoursed or in courses. Stones are taken more or less at random and built to form the strongest bonds across and vertically in the wall with no attempt to form accurate vertical or horizontal joints. Large stones are flat bedded and packed or wedged up with smaller stones. Joints are well filled with mortar and where these joints on the face are large they are packed with small stones driven into the gaps. The strength in these walls depends largely on the mortar.

Where stone can be quarried from thin beds in the quarry or where thick beds are easily split into smaller pieces the rubble can often be readily cut into squares. Such squared rubble, also known as square-snecked rubble, can then be built into uncoursed walls in irregular patterns involving units of four stones (a large stone known as a riser or jumper, two thinner stones called levellers and a smaller stone, a check or sneck). When the rubble is levelled up to form courses 300-450mm (12-18") deep coursed squared rubble is produced (Figures 6.1c-d). The squared rubble can be brought to courses of varying depths with some of the stones at course height

FIGURE 6.1A Random rubble wall: Flodden Wall at the Vennel [32]

The use of parallel laminated and cross-bedded sandstones, mainly from the Kinnesswood Formation, in a rubble wall.
A.A.McMillan (1997)

FIGURE 6.1B Rubble-built tenement: No.7 West Nicolson Street
R.J.Gillanders

and smaller stones filling in the spaces. Figure 6.1d shows a good example of snecked squared rubble at **Marischal Place**, Blackhall. In regularly coursed squared rubble the courses are again of varying height but the stones in any one course are all of the same height (Figure 6.1e). A decorative variation of this style of walling is seen in some of the surviving buildings on the west side of **George Square** [43] where some wider vertical joints have a series of black dolerite snecks in them (Chapter 7, Plate 3).

FIGURE 6.1c Coursed squared rubble: detail Squared rubble (stone cut into squares) brought to courses of varying depths with some of the stones at course height and smaller stones (snecks) filling in the spaces.
Crown Copyright: Royal Commission on the Ancient and Historical Monuments of Scotland.

Rubble walls were often left as bare stone, for example in Old Town tenements, but sometimes they received a dash of aggregate bound together with a lime binding agent (harling) or a smooth floated mortar finish (rendering) as can be seen on the north-west side of **St Andrew Square**.

Many buildings in Edinburgh's New Town were built of ashlar, sandstone blocks accurately dressed to given dimensions. The thickness of the joints between these stones is often as little as 3mm (2/16″) between courses 250-360mm (10-14″) high. Ashlar is generally built like regular coursed rubble (Figure 6.1f). Ashlar is the most expensive and best type of masonry. Often in Edinburgh, to reduce the cost, outside

Figure 6.1d Snecked squared rubble:
Marischal Place, Blackhall
Tenement gable end (built in 1905).
R.J.Gillanders (1998)

FIGURE 6.1E
Regular coursed
squared rubble: detail
Here, the courses of
squared rubble can be of
varying height but the
stones in any one course
are all of the same height.
Crown Copyright: Royal
Commission on the
Ancient and Historical
Monuments of Scotland.

walls were faced with ashlar (fixed to cheaper material, usually rubble, by bonding stones) on streets or front elevations.[3]

The ground floors of many buildings in Edinburgh's New Town are emphasised by the use of rusticated ashlar in which the margins of the stones are chamfered to form V-shaped channels along the joints, as on the north side of **Charlotte Square** [91] (Figure 6.1g-h). Alternatively ashlar edges are sunk to form channelled or rectangular joints. The latter are seen on the lower part of the **High Court of Justiciary** [14], Bank Street.

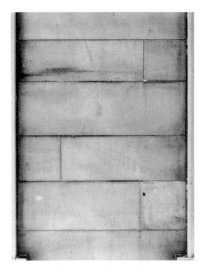

FIGURE 6.1F Polished ashlar: detail
Sandstone blocks accurately dressed to given dimensions.
Crown Copyright: Royal Commission on the Ancient and Historical Monuments of Scotland.

FIGURE 6.1G Polished, rusticated ashlar with V shaped channels along the joints: north side of Charlotte Square [91]
Crown Copyright: Reproduced Courtesy of Historic Scotland

FIGURE 6.1H Polished, rusticated ashlar with V shaped channels: detail
Crown Copyright: Royal Commission on the Ancient and Historical Monuments of Scotland.

FIGURE 6.1I Droved (boasted) work: detail
Crown Copyright: Royal Commission on the Ancient and Historical Monuments of Scotland.

SURFACE FINISHES

Smoothed ashlar

Ashlar blocks are worked on the exposed surface to produce a variety of surface finishes. A smoothed or polished face (e.g. Figure 6.1f) was produced by working the stone with a 50mm (2″) wide chisel (a boaster) to a regular surface then rubbing it with a carborundum, sand and water mixture till smooth. This process used to be done by hand and was very expensive but the use of mechanical 'rubbing beds' has made the production of this kind of surface finish much cheaper.[4] An Edinburgh building firm, Watherstone's was one of the first to use machinery for smoothing.[5] James Gowans, the Edinburgh quarrymaster and builder advocated the use of polished ashlar: 'Polishing removes the bruised material, and presents to wasting agents a surface more likely to prevent decay than any other kind of work'.[6]

Droved (boasted) work

This type of finish is very common in Edinburgh where the flat surface has been worked over with a 50mm (2″) chisel to give a series of 40-50mm wide bands of parallel tool marks over the surface. These can run horizontally, vertically (Figure 6.1i) or diagonally across the face.

Tooled work

When the boasted surface is further worked with an even broader chisel, 100mm (4″) wide, so that it is covered with continuous parallel horizontal, vertical or diagonal fine lines the finish is described as tooled. The spacing between the lines depends on the hardness of the stone.

Stugged (punched) work

Here the stone is worked over with a pointed chisel (punch). Often a droved margin is worked around this stone. With finer pits the surface is known as jabbed or picked. An example of coarse stugged work on squared rubble is shown in Figure 6.1c.

Broached work

Where the surface is worked with a narrow chisel (gouge) or a toothed chisel to form a series of horizontal or vertical furrows the result is broached work (Figure 6.1j). Usually these stones have chisel drafted margins.

Rock-faced (bull-faced, pitch-faced, rusticated) work

As the name suggests this is an attempt to reproduce the natural rock surface by producing a central rough raised area with a marginal draft (Figure 6.1k). Rock-face finishes are often seen in the basements of New Town buildings, for example in **Charlotte Square** and **Heriot Row**, with polished ashlar at higher elevations.

Vermiculated work

This finish produces a continuous winding pattern slightly raised above the inner area of the stone.[7] An example can be seen on the south side of the **Bank of Scotland** [13] on the Mound.

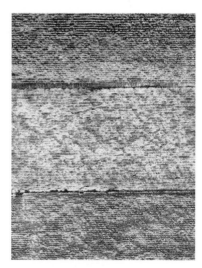

Figure 6.1j Broached work: detail
Crown Copyright: Royal Commission on the
Ancient and Historical Monuments of Scotland.

Figure 6.1k Rock-faced (Bull-faced, pitch-faced, rusticated) work: detail
Crown Copyright: Royal Commission on the
Ancient and Historical Monuments of Scotland.

CLADDING

Sandstone is still used in building today as cladding to steel-framed buildings to give the appearance of traditional stonework. This stone is usually prepared at a factory where the sandstone is machine cut and dressed prior to delivery to the building site. There, the main work consists in fixing the prepared stone to the building. Since the Second World War the stone veneer on modern buildings has been made thinner so that it is now often no more than 100mm thick. Thinner and lighter skins require very good anchorage to the building where in the past the mass of the stone helped to keep the cladding in place. Modern cladding is thus held on by large numbers of non-ferrous fixings including ties, clamps and dowels of copper, phosphor-bronze or stainless steel.[8]

USE OF DIFFERENT STONE IN THE SAME BUILDING

Commonly stones of different character and from different sources are used in the same building. The **Meadows Pillars** and **Sundial** [158] (Figures 6.2 and 6.3) are probably the most extreme examples in Edinburgh. They were erected in 1886 by James Gowans[9] to commemorate the International Exhibition, possibly to serve as an indication of the weathering properties of a range of stones which were being 'imported' to the city. A wide range of stones from Scotland and England and several types of stone finish can be seen. The only local examples are blocks from Hailes and Redhall quarries. Unfortunately the pillars have since been moved and re-erected, so that the original structure and the order in which the stones were placed has been changed. They may now be seen at the west end of Melville Drive, south of Tollcross, at the entrance to West Meadow Park.

In these monuments, amongst stones from further afield, there are blocks of *Dundee Formation* sandstone from Myreton and Leoch quarries, near Dundee, *Cementstone Group* sandstone from Whitsome Newton, Berwickshire, *Lower Limestone Group* sandstone from Woodburn and Parkhead, Northumberland and *Middle Limestone Group* sandstone from Cocklaw, Northumberland. Most of these, said to be weathering in 1893,[10] have not weathered much more since then. On the Sundial the Whitsome Newton stone is scaling and cracking slightly but much of the detail of the lettering and coats of arms on the Permian red sandstone from Ballochmyle near Mauchline, Ayrshire has been lost. In the Pillars the younger Permo-Triassic sandstones have generally not stood so well as

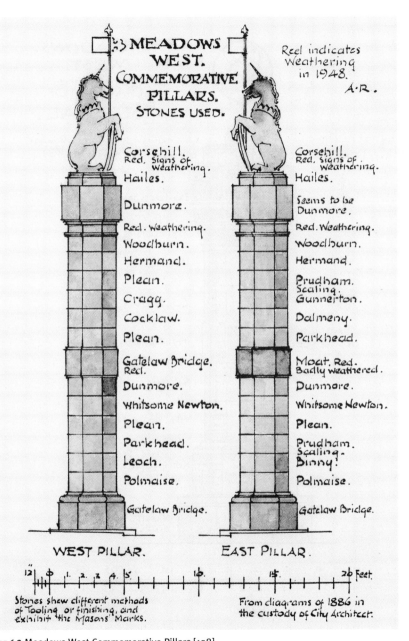

FIGURE 6.2 Meadows West Commemorative Pillars [158]
Andrew Rollo's drawing (1948) based on diagrams made in 1886.
Crown Copyright: Royal Commission on the Ancient and Historical Monuments of Scotland.

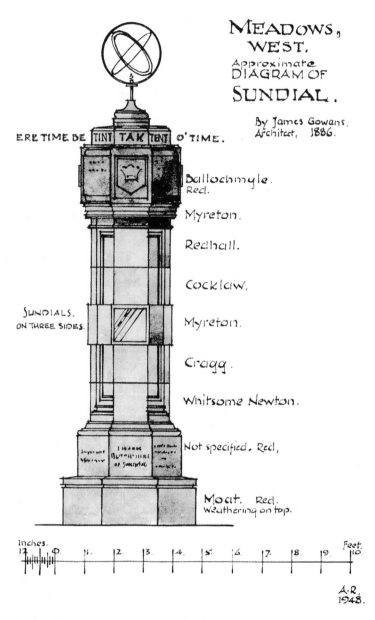

FIGURE 6.3 Meadows West Commemorative Sundial [158]
Andrew Rollo's drawing (1948) based on diagrams made in 1886.
Crown Copyright: Royal Commission on the Ancient and Historical Monuments of Scotland

those of the Lower Carboniferous. However the fact that stones of different hardness and grain-size have been placed together in the Pillars may account for some of the differential weathering observed. Equally, weathering effects in adjacent stones of different composition may have been increased by chemical run-off over the years.

The use of red and pale brown, yellow or grey sandstones in the same building is commonly seen throughout the city, particularly in houses and villas built during the last 100 years in the outer districts. Generally the Permian red sandstones provided cut blocks for use as smoothed ashlar quoins and jambs with the paler coloured Carboniferous stones used in wall courses in a range of finishes.

AVAILABILITY OF STONE: AN HISTORICAL PERSPECTIVE

At the height of the building boom in the early 19th century, Edinburgh's quarries could not keep up with the demand for sandstone so that the builders had to turn to nearby areas outside the city. In fact, this was not a new practice as stone had been shipped over from the Fife ports of Culross during the early 16th century[11] and Burntisland in the late 18th century.[12] The introduction of new forms of transport, including firstly canal routes and later the railways, made it easier to bring stone from further afield (Figure 6.4).

The first large supplies of stone came from the West Lothian quarries of Humbie and Binny which were located near to the Union Canal (opened in 1822). The canal trade declined with the growth of the railway network from 1842 onwards. More quarries were brought into use by Edinburgh builders exploiting the new railways. The cream and white stones of Polmaise, Plean and Dunmore came from the west. The deep red stone from the ancient quarries of Corncockle, Locharbriggs, Gatelawbridge, Moat and Corsehill was transported on the Caledonian Railway from the south-west. The completion of the Forth Railway Bridge in 1890 made it easier to bring the white and yellow Fife sandstones (from Grange and Fordell) into Edinburgh, although the old Cullalo and Longannet quarries had been supplying stone for many decades. However, as demand for sandstone decreased, the Scottish quarries faced competition from the large quarries in northern England, in particular Prudham, Gunnerton, Doddington and Cragg, all of which supplied stone to Edinburgh in the closing years of the 19th century.

Probably the inherent conservatism in stone working methods which had remained essentially the same for hundreds of years contributed to the decline in the use of stone. Cheaply produced brick and artificial stone slowly began to replace sandstone before the First World War. More rapid house building led to the replacement of sandstone by

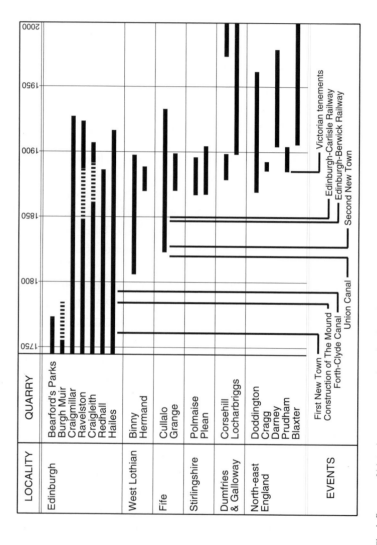

FIGURE 6.4 The influence of historic events upon the selection of stone for Edinburgh's buildings.
Each bar shows the approximate duration of quarrying activity for a selection of important sources. Most of the local Edinburgh quarries yielded stone prior to 1750. For other sources, the earliest approximate date of supply to Edinburgh is shown. Some of these quarries have an earlier history (Appendix 4).

brick, firstly for party walls, then for the backs, sides and chimneys of houses. Latterly it was only ground floor fronts, and last of all, dressings for windows and doors which used natural stone. By the late 1930s even dressings were being made from artificial stone.[13]

The decline in demand for building stone was a self-perpetuating process. Throughout the 1920s and 1930s lessening demand meant that fewer men were employed and thus the body of the workforce, with hard-won experience required to work stone, diminished at a steadily increasing rate. Falling or fluctuating output led to uneconomic use of quarry plant and labour. The last straw was probably the outbreak of the Second World War when men left the industry which was not protected from the effects of conscription into the armed forces.[14] Many quarries which closed then have never reopened.

When the post-war rebuilding programme began in 1945 the shortage of stone workers was offset to some extent by increased mechanisation in stone handling. Nevertheless, by 1949 it was estimated that surviving Scottish quarries were producing less than a quarter of the output needed to minimise costs.[15] The need for a quick, cheap, craft-free building programme contributed to a change of attitude towards what was expected of the building industry. As a result, the use of natural stone declined to such an extent that by 1950 only eight sandstone quarries were being worked in Scotland.[16] Although sandstone continued to be used for fronts of buildings or as a facing stone, it was the Northumberland quarries at Blaxter and Darney which became the important sources of supply in the post-war years.

From the early 1970s government and private owners have shown a renewed interest in the use of sandstone for the restoration of historic buildings and the cladding of new buildings. As a result, particularly for restoration purposes, matching natural stone has had to be found either from currently working quarries or from buildings which have been demolished in recent years. Ten years ago according to Elaine Leary,[17] Bob Heath (pers.comm.) and BGS sources,[18] up to eleven sandstone quarries were working in Scotland, namely Clashach, Corncockle, Corsehill, Cutties Hillock, new Dunmore, Greenbrae, Locharbriggs, Newbigging, Rosebrae, Spittal (for flagstone) and Spynie. Some of these were worked intermittently to meet the demand for specific building projects. Several of these together with quarries operating in northern England, including Catcastle, Dunhouse, Springwell, Stainton, Stanton Moor, Stoke Hall, Wellfield and Woodkirk, have supplied the city in recent years. Today, a similar number is operational[19] (Appendix 2), demonstrating there is a continuing demand for top quality stone. Snatch quarrying in which stone is extracted from temporary excavations, for use in new build or for repair work, has become a practical method. Thus the temporary excavation in September 1997 near the former Binny Quarry, West Lothian (Harry Turnbull, Stirling Stone Group, pers. comm.) has supplied sufficient material for repairs to the Scott Monument [3], Princes Street.

In Edinburgh the local sandstone quarrying industry is extinct. However, the need for restoration of the city's priceless architectural heritage means that there will always be a market, as long as the resource from farther afield is available. In turn, the continuing demand for sandstone should ensure that the skills required to quarry and work the stone will not be lost. In Scotland generally, the building stone industry is showing signs of revival and the environmental benefits and low consumption of production energy may encourage even greater use of the resource in the 21st century.[20]

REFERENCES

1. Gowans, J., *The Builder*, 1883, p.87.
2. Craig, G.Y., in Gifford, J., McWilliam, C., Walker, D., *The buildings of Scotland, Edinburgh*, London: Penguin Books, 1984, p.24.
3. Davey, A., Heath, B., Hodges, D., Milne, R., Palmer, M., *The care and conservation of Georgian houses - a maintenance manual for the New Town of Edinburgh*, Edinburgh New Town Conservation Committee, 1978, p.62-63.
4. McKay, W.B., *Building construction*, 1, London: Longmans, Green and Co., 1948, p.37-39.
5. Bremner, D., *The industries of Scotland*, Edinburgh: Adam and Charles Black, 1869, p.416.
6. Gowans, J., *The Builder*, 1883, p.88.
7. McKay, W.B., *op.cit.*
8. Ashurst, J., and Dimes, F.G., *Stone in building: its use and potential today*, London: Architectural Press, 1977, p.33-34.
9. Gowans, Sir J., The Memorial Masons' Pillars in *Model dwelling houses*, Edinburgh: T. and A. Constable, 1886, p.55-57.
10. Craig, G., Building stones used in Edinburgh: their geological sources, relative durability and other characteristics, *Transactions of the Edinburgh Geological Society*, 6, 1893, p.266-68.
11. *Accounts of the Masters of Works*, 1, (1529-1615), p.2, 3, 5, 7, 13.
12. *Council Record*, 116, (1790), p.364.
13. Broughton, H.F., Illingworth, J.R., and Rice, G.G., Survey of building in sandstone in Scotland, *National Building Studies Special Report No. 20*, 1953, p.3.
14. *Report of H.M. Inspectors of Mines and Quarries for the years 1939-49*, HMSO, 1950, p.5.
15. Broughton, H.F., Illingworth, J.R. and Rice, G.G., *op.cit.*, p.11.
16. *ibid.*, p.10.

17. Leary, E., *The building sandstones of the British Isles*, Watford: Building Research Establishment, 1986, p.8-9.

18. Harris, P.M., Highley, D. E. and Bentley, K.R. (compilers), *Directory of mines and quarries 1988: 2nd edition*. Keyworth, Nottinghamshire: British Geological Survey, 1988.

19. Cameron, D.G., Highley, D.E., Hillier, J.A., Johnson, T.P., Linley, K.A., Mills, A.J., Smith, C.G. and White R.G. (compilers), *Directory of mines and quarries: Digital data: 01/04/98*, Keyworth, Nottingham: British Geological Survey, 1998.

20. Hutton & Rostron, *A future for stone in Scotland*. Research Report, Edinburgh: Historic Scotland, 1997.

CHAPTER 7 | WHERE TO SEE SANDSTONES IN EDINBURGH'S BUILDINGS: PART 1. EDINBURGH'S QUARRIES AND THEIR BUILDING STONE PRODUCTS

"For situation and durability of its building materials, few cities have equal advantages to Edinburgh, and there is, perhaps, no town of which the general and distant effects are more picturesque and striking"

THOMAS SHEPHERD, 1829.[1]

This and the following chapter describe representative sandstones used in Edinburgh. A brief history of the principal quarries is presented together with a selection of buildings where building stone may be seen to advantage fairly near the centre of the city. The use of local igneous rocks is also discussed.

Documentary evidence for the use of particular sandstones is variable. Even where it is known that a specific sandstone was utilised in a building it is not always possible to confirm that it was the only one used or ascertain to which phase of building the documentary evidence relates. In buildings constructed of more than one sandstone it can be difficult to distinguish between them, especially if the building is in an uncleaned state or has not been carefully cleaned. The quarry sources for most of the buildings (listed in Table 1.1 and Appendix 3) are documented or have been obtained from architects or restorers currently using the stones in Edinburgh.

The early sandstone quarries were often temporary features situated around the houses and lands within or immediately outside the town walls. Permission to open quarries was usually granted on condition that they were filled in later. It is not always possible to locate precisely workings despite mention of them in some of the earliest Town Council Records. The first houses were built on the ridge to the east of the Castle and were seldom more than two storeys high. They were constructed of timber obtained from the nearby forest and thatched with straw. The fire risks were so great that, in 1425, the third Parliament of James I introduced laws designed to reduce the number of conflagrations.[2] Henceforth most building was to be in stone.

From the mid 18th century, with the building of the New Town of Edinburgh beyond the constraints of the old town walls, the old quarries could not produce the block sizes, quality and quantities of stone demanded by architects and developers for the larger and more prestigious buildings. As a result, quarries developed on the west side of the city, most notably at Craigleith, Ravelston, Redhall and Hailes (Figure 3.1).

The principal local building sandstones in Edinburgh were obtained from the Carboniferous formations (Table 3.1, Figure 3.1). Sandstones within the *Kinnesswood Formation* were formerly worked at Craigmillar,[3] the Grange district and in the Meadows and Bruntsfield areas (the Burgh Muir). *Ballagan Formation* sandstones were obtained from the Camstone quarries, east of Salisbury Crags in Holyrood Park, and at Dumbiedykes, Society and many other quarries in the Old Town. The Salisbury Crags Sill (dolerite intruded into strata of the *Ballagan Formation*) was also quarried. Much of west and north Edinburgh is underlain by strata of the *Gullane Formation*.[4] Three main stratigraphical units, namely the *Craigleith*, *Ravelston* and *Hailes* sandstones, have been worked extensively in parts of the New Town and the western outskirts of the city.[5] Smaller quantities of building sandstones from the *Limestone Coal Formation* and *Upper Limestone Formation* were quarried at Joppa and Niddrie.

STONES FROM THE KINNESSWOOD FORMATION

The oldest known quarries worked in Edinburgh exploited sandstones in the *Kinnesswood Formation* (formerly classified as part of the Upper Old Red Sandstone) of late Devonian to early Carboniferous age. These quarries worked sandstones of a variety of colours ranging from white through buff to light brownish-grey to pink and red.

Burgh Muir (Meadows and Bruntsfield) and Grange Quarries

The Bruntsfield and Meadows area was covered in early historical times by the dense oak forest of Drumselch. Here, a large tract of land, the Burgh Muir, was gifted to the City by King David I in the early 12th century. The Burgh Muir, also known as the Common Muir, stretched southwards from the south bank of the Burgh Loch (now the Meadows) to the Jordan Burn. In 1508 concern was felt about the lack of supervision of the use of the Burgh Muir. As a result James IV granted the Town Council power to lease the Burgh Muir subject to the condition that the lessees were to use the Burgh market, set up brew houses and provide beer for the city ale houses. From then on, citizens were encouraged to cut trees and use the wood in building their houses in the Old Town. As the Burgh Muir was cleared, so parts of the area came to be quarried for the soft grey (sic) sandstone which was used for building in Edinburgh and Leith.[6] In 1554, eleven quarriers were ordered not to work quarries on 'the common muir of the burgh' unless the workings were kept 20 feet (6m) from paths. They were also ordered to fill in any holes dug, a regulation which the Town Council had great difficulty in enforcing. The Council also had responsibility for setting the price of stone including those for sill and lintel, long and arch work.[7] Mill stones were also taken from time to time.[8]

We cannot identify many buildings constructed of stones from the Burgh Muir. However, it is almost certain that the late 15th century tower house of **Merchiston Castle** (incorporated in **Napier University**, No.10 Colinton Road) was built mainly from local sandstone.[9] In the **Vennel**, the tower and adjacent part of the

Flodden Wall [32] (Figure 6.1a) which connects Lauriston Place with the Grassmarket, were constructed of stones from Burgh Muir, Ravelston and Hailes quarries.[10] Town Council Records show that stones from the Burgh Muir as well as from the Granton quarries were used in the construction of the **Leith Bulwark** in 1555.[11]

The regulation of quarrying in the Burgh Muir proved no easy task for the City Fathers, despite the severe penalties which they imposed for unauthorised quarrying. In 1597-98, the penalty for such work (or the illegal selling of mill stones) could be imprisonment in irons for 40 days, scourging, branding on the cheek or banishment.[12] At that time the Town Council handed over half of the Links to the Fellowship and Society of Brewers who then took over most of the rest and built walls round it. Throughout the 17th century the Council had continued to try to regulate the use of quarries, putting up boundary markers between the workings, setting the price for stones and vainly ordering the quarriers to fill up the holes. In 1638, the Burgh Muir was one of the many areas which provided stone for **Parliament House** [21] although it was soon replaced by Ravelston Quarry as a source of supply.[13] In 1646 the City Treasurer was authorised to pay Robert Gray 400 merks (£266 Scots) for loss sustained by him when his quarry was used as a burial ground during the previous year's outbreak of the plague.[14]

The Town Council continued to make things difficult for themselves by authorising an agreement, dated 25th December 1695, in which they allowed the tenants of the Burgh Loch and Bruntsfield Links areas to quarry 'ane aiker' of their choice on any part of the Links.[15] The occasional apparent chaos had its positive side in that, by 1695, the Links were well established as a 'place where the neighbours play golf'[16] using unfilled quarry holes and spoil heaps as obstacles instead of bunkers. When they rode the City boundaries in May 1701, the City Fathers noted that several quarries in the Links were not filled in 'and therby not only spoyled the gouff but endanger the passingers contrair to the tenor of the tack of the Links'.[17]

Most of the references in the Town Council Records are to quarries in the Wester Burgh Muir, but old maps from the 1850s and earlier show many sites to the south of the Burgh Loch, some of which are likely to have been opened in the 17th or 18th centuries.[18] Quarrying in the Wester Burgh Muir and part of the Links continued well into the 18th century. Traces of one of the excavations, the 'City Quarry', may be seen as a large hollow near the putting green, west of Alvanley Terrace and Warrender Park Terrace.[19] This quarry supplied stone between 1739 and 1743 for the

Charity Workhouse [34] (later the headquarters of the 4th and 5th Royal Scots) which was built on the west side of the present Forrest Road.[20] Today's tenements on the right hand side of Forrest Hill represent the altered remains of the north wing of the Workhouse. In 1741 stone was used from Bruntsfield for the rebuilding of the tenements at the Luckenbooths. Most other traces of quarrying in that area seem to have been removed in a general tidying up exercise which provided work for the unemployed during the depression of 1816-17, although some traces survived until 1884 when the Marchmont tenements were being built. Most of the stone for the frontages of these buildings came from greater distances but the feu charters permitted that some local stone could be used for other parts of their construction.

About 1883, quarries were opened up at the south end of Marchmont Road on the east side to provide rubble for the backs of the tenements.[21] Quarries at **Dick Place** had previously been opened to provide stone for the building of houses there in c.1864.

Some of the old quarries posed problems where they obstructed the line of a street or foundations. The Burgh Engineer was required to indicate such areas to prospective developers. Construction of buildings on the west side of Marchmont Road, south of its junction with Warrender Park Road, was held up for ten years after 1890 to allow for settlement of quarry fill. In an attempt to speed up the infilling of these quarries, free tipping was encouraged by advertisements which appeared in the newspapers of the 1880s.[22]

Widespread use of local stone of the *Kinnesswood Formation*, not only from the Burgh Muir but also Craigmillar can be seen in several other areas on the south side of Edinburgh. Notable examples of buildings constructed of stones from these sources include the tenements on the north side of the **Lawnmarket** and in **Mound Place**. Small local quarries supplied much of the pink and red rubble used in the old boundary walls on the south side of the city, particularly in the Grange - Blackford area.

Craigmillar and Hawkhill Wood Quarries

At the Craigmillar quarries (Figure 3.1), the rock is a compact, pebbly quartzose sandstone, typically red to pale brown. At Hawkhill Wood Quarry a very light mauve/pink to fine yellow/buff stone was worked mainly for rubble work and this colour was regarded as the best building stone. The sandstone contains occasional bands of marl, thin calcareous cornstones (former soil horizons) and conglomerates.

As early as the 14th century, quarries at Craigmillar were providing stone for the building of **Craigmillar Castle**. The castle sits on an outcrop of the same stone. In 1532, stone from Craigmillar quarries was used in the building of the **Palace of Holyrood** [146]. At first, corbels and ashlar were supplied. Later, stones were used for the serving hatch of the kitchen and flagstones to cover water conduits.[23] Fourteen large stones were dug in 1555 for the gate at the Priestfield side of the King's Park.[24] In July 1636, Craigmillar stone was brought into town for the **Parliament House** [21][25] and again in 1639 for work on **Edinburgh Castle** [9].[26] The quarries seem to have been worked fairly continuously as they were used as a source of rubble for the courtyard interior of **George Heriot's School** [33] (1628-60), Lauriston Place,[27] and again for George Square [43] in the 1760s.[28] The stone was hard to work and often used in the rubble form typically seen in the backs of most of the surviving houses in the west side of **George Square** (1766-85). On the west side of George Square [43], the buildings up to **No.27** (built 1767-75) (see detail of **No.20** in Plate 3) and **No.60** [45] at the north end of the east side are built of coursed squared rubble from Craigmillar of various hues, with dark coloured dolerite snecks from the old quarries in the Salisbury Crags.[29] The rest of the east side used Craigleith stone. The colour of the Craigmillar stone is variable ranging from grey through yellow to orange to pink. The sandstone was often used in very large blocks which have not weathered badly where laid parallel to the natural bedding surfaces. However, some of the blocks, which were laid on edge, are scaling.

By the time the Second Statistical Account was published in 1845, the quarries had closed. From then on, working seems to have been intermittent until 1892 when the stone's use was restricted mainly to that for kerb stones.[30] The Quarry List records one quarry working in 1901-02 and then in 1908, by which time six men were employed. In 1906 another quarry was worked at Craigmillar and continued in operation intermittently until 1914 but latterly with only one man. After the First World War, one or two quarries operated from time to time, with 21 men in the Hawkhill Wood Quarry[31] in 1937. The last year in which Craigmillar appeared in the Quarry List was 1956. Several of the quarries can still be seen but others have been infilled.

The stone quarried at Craigmillar was considered relatively impermeable to water which led to its use in the construction of the Edinburgh Reservoirs and in **Leith Docks** (1894-96).

Hawkhill Wood Quarry provided stone for villas on the south side of Edinburgh in the 1920s, for example at **Mayfield Road**, **Esslemont Road** and **Ross Road**, using face stone from Braehead Quarry at Fauldhouse.[32] A fine example of rubble from Hawkhill Wood can be seen at the **Reid Memorial Church** (1929-33), West Savile Terrace, where it is used with ashlar from Doddington. Stone from an unspecified quarry at Craigmillar (though probably Hawkhill Wood) was used at **Fairmilehead Parish Church** (1937-38), Frogston Road West, along with Doddington ashlar.

STONE FROM THE BALLAGAN FORMATION
The 'Salisbury' Quarries (Camstone and Dumbiedykes)

Early quarrying of sandstones of the *Ballagan Formation* also took place in Holyrood Park. It seems likely that the Camstone Quarries east of Salisbury Crags, together with other workings such as those at Dumbiedykes, west of the Crags, provided the stone for **Holyrood Palace** [146] between 1529 and 1536. Wall stones, newels, arch stones and stones for gutters were taken from these 'Salisbury Quarries' (presumed to include the Camstone Quarry) for the north range, the present north-west tower and the west and south ranges of the quadrangle of the Palace. In December 1532 local stones were used for a great oven in the Palace although the base of the oven used material from North Berwick (probably a basaltic rock rather than a sandstone). Sir William MacDowell was an overseer of these quarries between July and November, 1536. Sledges were used to carry stones between the quarry and the building work at Holyrood. Sometimes these sledges were hauled by horses but often men were used.[33] The proximity of the Salisbury quarries to Holyrood and the intervening sloping ground would certainly have made sledges easy to use. In 1748 part of the Royal Park was let to George Knox with 'liberty to open and work stone quarries' and he did this between 1755 and 1757. In the late 18th century stone from Salisbury quarries was used to build the 'Bridewell' on Calton Hill, and to pave the Regent Road and Waterloo Place between 1810 and 1820. The 'Bridewell' had been founded by the Earl of Morton, the Grand Master of Scotland in 1791 and was the first of the prisons on the Calton Hill.

Salisbury Crags Quarries

At Salisbury Crags in Holyrood Park some of Edinburgh's oldest quarries worked the dolerite sill (a hard, coarse-grained, dark grey igneous rock). This durable rock, locally known as whinstone, was used extensively as 'calsey stanes' for the streets of

Edinburgh. The stone was used as rubble in buildings on the south side of Edinburgh. Rubble used at **No. 82 Nicolson Street** [40] (late 18th century) (Figure 2.9) and snecks at **Nos. 16-22 George Square** [43] are likely to be from these quarries. Occasional blocks of dolerite are seen as in **No. 20 George Square** (Plate 3).

The earls of Haddington were the hereditary keepers of the Royal Park of Holyrood and, over nearly 200 years to 1845 during which they held that office, permitted gradually increasing quarrying activity. This reached a peak during the first twenty years of the 19th century. So much stone was taken for paving the streets of Edinburgh, London and other cities that considerable alarm was expressed at the damage being inflicted on the Crags. The situation became so serious that legal action was taken to prevent further deterioration, but the case dragged on for twelve years, first in the Court of Session in February 1819 'to restrain certain operations authorised or conducted by Lord Haddington tending materially to the detriment' of the Royal Park. In September 1831 the House of Lords concluded that the Earl of Haddington had no right of title to work quarries in the Royal Park. In 1845 the 9th Earl was paid £30,674 sterling as compensation for surrender of the office of Hereditary Keeper.[34]

Greyfriar's Port Quarries

Greyfriar's Port, afterwards called Society or Bristo Port, was situated outwith the City Wall at the junction of Candlemaker Row and the present George IV Bridge. Quarries were present there in the early 16th century, since it is recorded that in October 1530 a woman, Katryne Heriot, was ordered to be drowned in one of the quarry holes. She was convicted for theft and for 'bringing of this contagious sickness from Leith to this town and breaking the statutes made thereupon'.[35] Twenty-three years later, James Henrison was ordered by the Town Council to stop quarrying there and fill up the holes.[36] Stone was still being taken in 1583 and then in 1585 the Town Council made Andrew Slater, College Master of Works, responsible for filling up the holes.[37]

The Society Quarry (possibly one of the Greyfriars Port quarries) lay close to the west end of present-day Chambers Street. It belonged to the Fellowship and Society of Brewers[38] and provided rubble for the preliminary work on nearby **Parliament House** [21] from the spring of 1632 and throughout 1633. In 1632 two quarriers were employed, each earning 66/8d Scots per week. Twelve labourers, working with them, were paid 30/- Scots each. The next year the quarriers received £4 Scots per week.[39] The quarries in the Society Yard are mentioned again twenty years later when space was allocated for bakers' ovens.[40]

Other Old Town Quarries

Several other quarry sites lie within the Old Town but cannot be located precisely. In May 1581, a quarry on the land belonging to the Justice Clerk was used for repairs to the town wall in the Blackfriars and Cowgate Port area.[41] The Town's College had its own quarry which was in use in May 1670.[42] Further south, Windmill Lane, connecting Chapel Street to George Square is near the site of a 17th century quarry which supplied stones for the use of the town. Nearby, a windmill was used to pump water from the Burgh Loch for local breweries. The quarry may have been the same one which was leased from time to time eighty years later, when it was rented by a mason who hired a quarryman and two barrowmen. Part of the condition of his seven-year let was that three feet of best earth was to be laid on top of the quarry rubbish. The quarry gave its name to Quarry Close near the junction of West Crosscauseway and Chapel Street.[43]

STONE FROM THE GULLANE FORMATION
Craigleith

The *Craigleith Sandstone*, within the *Gullane Formation* (Figure 3.4), attains a maximum thickness of 107m and comprises a highly siliceous, close-textured, fine-grained, grey sandstone.[44] As well as having been worked at Craigleith Quarry (Figures 3.5 to 3.6; Plate 1), it was also worked at Craigcrook, Maidencraig and Granton (Sea and Land) quarries. The principal Ravelston quarry, situated between Craigcrook and Maidencraig quarries, also worked *Craigleith Sandstone*. Stone from Barnton Park was marketed as 'Craigleith' but this quarry is possibly situated at a higher horizon.[45] Numerous ancient quarries worked this sandstone in the New Town, for example those in Bearford's Parks, Upper Quarry Holes and possibly Broughton.

The *Craigleith Sandstone* was most extensively worked at Craigleith, 2 miles (3 km) west of the city centre, where a highly siliceous fine-grained sandstone was worked. Two types of stone were worked at Craigleith Quarry. The very hard, fine-grained, cream-coloured, compact sandstone, known as 'liver rock', was used for the fronts of the best houses and public buildings, where it could be given a very smooth surface and was also worked into delicate mouldings and other kinds of architectural decoration. The easily worked 'common' or 'feak' rock (thinly bedded, greyish-white, silty sandstone) could also sometimes be used for the best building work. More often it was utilised in rubble work, foundations, stair steps, plats and paving.[46] The stone characteristically has fine wispy cross-lamination, sometimes carbonaceous, with occasional brown clay ironstone concretions. The stone was described as 'well nigh imperishable' and was used extensively not only in Edinburgh but also in London, the United States and in Europe.[47, 48] George Smith concluded in 1835, 'Craigleith stands pre-eminently, not only as to extent, by constantly yielding an abundant supply of every variety of sizes at all times, but as to beauty of colour, and, above all, the durability of the stone'.[49]

Hull (1872) records that the sandstone at Craigleith Quarry, occurred in beds varying from a few inches to 12 feet (4m), interrupted with shales and showing a vertical depth of about 250 feet (76m).[50] Anderson, writing in 1938, noted that at one time the quarry face at Craigleith was said to have been 110m deep of which the bottom 104m was solid rock.[51] The top 6m of 'fakes [siltstones] and sandstone bands' and top 15m of solid rock were apparently not used for building purposes.

The first records of the use of Craigleith stone are in the Accounts of the Masters of Works. In January 1615, quarriers were paid at the quarry which was then known as Innerleith or Enderleith,[52] for producing 200 double arch stones for **Edinburgh Castle** [9]. The stone was taken to the Castle in the King's own carts during this period of activity which lasted until 1619, but sometimes independent carriers were used. Thomas Young, the local farmer, was paid £17-6-8d Scots for damage to his ground and spoiling of his grass on various occasions up to September 1615 and again in 1616. Craigleith supplied stone of all kinds for the Castle and some for **Holyrood Palace** [146] in 1616. Besides ashlar, double arch, 'great lintels' and coping stones, a great stone 'for working the Kingis armes on' was won for the Castle in September 1616. Quarriers, who worked at Craigleith in this early phase of its operation, had to pay a toll or 'gaitmail' for their passage between the quarry and the High Street which was refunded to them.[53]

The quarry produced both liver rock and common rock.[54] From time to time, huge blocks of sandstone were excavated. For example, in 1791 stones were won for the six pillars at the main entrance of the **Old College** [28] (1789–1828), University of Edinburgh, South Bridge (Plate 4). Each pillar measures 6.8m (22 feet) in height and 0.98m (3 feet 3 inches) diameter at the base. Sixteen horses were required to haul each stone, placed on a special carriage. Considerable doubt was expressed as to whether the old North Bridge would stand up to each load, since each pillar weighed nine tons.[55] In 1823, probably the biggest ever block was excavated. It measured 41.5m (136 feet) by 6.1m (20 feet) and its calculated weight was quoted as 1500 tons (1524 tonnes). It was conveyed in large blocks to the Calton Hill and forms the architrave of the unfinished **National Monument** [140] (see below). The remainder was sent by sea to Buckingham Palace.[56]

According to George Smith, 'it may be well said that the New Town of Edinburgh has been built from the material of Craigleith',[57] and it was during its building that the quarry witnessed its maximum activity. The period 1817-1827 seems to have been especially busy as the quarry yielded £45,000 sterling in rent. Shepherd shows it as it was in 1829 in his engraving.[58] By 1835 the quarry was rented by George Johnston who shortened and improved the access road. In that year 60 carts were each making an average of four journeys per day into the City from Craigleith and the shortening of the road by a mile enabled a fifth journey to be undertaken. Little gunpowder was used in this quarry, most of the stone being got out by wedges. Johnston also built a railway from the floor up the quarry bank and used two horses to lift 120 tons (122 tonnes) of quarry waste out each day. Only six men were required with this arrangement and it took only five minutes to draw up and empty a wagon at the top.[59]

In such a large quarry, it is likely that flooding was always a problem. In the early part of the 19th century the quarry was kept clear of water by a pump driven by a horse in a gin.[60] A water-colour painted by James Skene in 1837 shows part of the quarry flooded then. By 1849 a description of Craigleith mentions 'two or three cots, at various heights, with the beams of steam engines projecting'.[61] It seems, therefore, that by the mid-19th century, steam power was used to keep the quarry dry.

At some stage during the 19th century, Craigleith Quarry was said to have been 110m (360 feet) deep. The quarry 'from its precipitous edges made you feel dizzy'.[62] Although activity declined after the 1850s the quarry was nevertheless recorded as 61m (200 feet) deep and covered 7 acres (2.8 hectares) in 1892.[63]

The true value of the Craigleith Quarry and its stone was not always appreciated. In the 1780s when the land containing the quarry changed hands, a large sum of money was returned to the purchaser for the lost space of ground occupied by the 'useless hill at Craigleith'.[64] Until the building boom of the 1820s, Craigleith Quarry cost only £50 sterling per year to rent. In 1805, when the feuers of Charlotte Square were building their houses they petitioned the Town Council to be allowed to use stone from Redhall Quarry. They stated that Craigleith or Ravelston stone, which was specified in the conditions of sale of feus, was not available in sufficient amounts for their extensive frontages and also indicated that 'it is well known to any person concerned in the building profession that Craigleith is a stone not of the most durable quality'. They suggested that the **Old College** [28], **Register House** [128] and even parts already built on the north side of Charlotte Square were already showing signs of weathering.[65] The tacksmen of Craigleith were quick to protest and refute the charges made about the quality of their product.[66] Eventually, the Town Council supported them and instructed the feuers to carry on with their buildings 'in conformity to the Articles of Roup on which they purchased their building lots'.[67] After 1807, the Articles and Conditions of Roup and Sale of Charlotte Square allowed the houses in the recesses of intermediate spaces to be 'done in Redhall stone, polished or any of the above mentioned (Craigleith, Craigcrook or Ravelston) but the whole intermediate space, in each range, to be done with one kind of stone'.[68] Thus only the north side of **Charlotte Square** [91] (1794-98) is entirely built of Craigleith stone (Figure 6.1g).

Craigleith was a hard and difficult stone to excavate and dress and its decline in use may be due to its hardness and the fact that the saw would not 'stand up' to it. As early as 1845, it was stated that 'Craigleith stone is now seldom used in Edinburgh but for parts requiring extra hardness, the Binny stone having superseded it.'[69] The coloured lithograph by William Leitch (Plate 1) and the earliest photographs of the quarry (Figures 3.5 and 3.6) show how the quarry looked in the1850s. By 1866, according to Bremner, 'now little stone is being drawn from it, demand being met more cheaply by softer stone obtained from various quarters . . . it is still preferred for steps and plats in staircases.'[70]

As early as Victorian times, doctors were drawing attention to the health hazards of working sandstone, particularly that from Craigleith. Dr Alison noted in 1852 that 'an old Craigleith man was done at 30, died at 35.'[71] He recommended that the men should grow beards and moustaches which would act as respirators. In 1854 Dr Wilson (first Director of the Industrial Museum, later to become the Royal Museum of Scotland) was noting that the trouble lay in the fine irritating sandstone powder and not, as the stoneworkers believed, in the sulphur in the stone. He added that what was needed was some 'contrivance for blowing away the dust as they have in Manchester cotton-mills.'[72]

According to Craig, writing of Craigleith stone in 1893, 'no houses are built entirely of it now, and it is used principally for steps, foundations and rubble'.[73] The lower rock was then being used for monuments, grindstones and glass cutting. The last major project for which Craigleith building stone was used was construction work begun in about 1895 for **Leith Docks**. At that time, work was concentrated in a second quarry which lay immediately to the north-east of the main working. This quarry, which was separated from the main working by a fault, was worked intermittently during the first 40 years of the 20th century. Here, the liver rock was reached at just over 26m (85 feet) depth.[74] In 1895 more than 90 men were employed but this number gradually fell. By 1900, 40 men were employed. By 1905 when working stopped, the number of workers was 25[75] and the stone was only used for rubble work and finally only for glass cutting.[76] During the First World War the deserted quarry was put to a new use. In 1915 demands for T.N.T. increased and because sulphuric acid was manufactured within the City, the production of the explosive could be accomplished comparatively easily. Consequently, the Lothian Chemical Company started to manufacture T.N.T. but because it was considered to be unsafe to prepare high explosive in a populated area a more remote site was chosen, namely the yards of Craigleith Quarry, on the outskirts of the City. Output of T.N.T. continued until the end of the War. The quality of the explosive reached a high standard, and towards the end of hostilities, the efficiency of the factory was the highest in the country.[77]

Although quarrying recommenced in 1922, work declined. By 1937, only 12 men were employed. All work is assumed to have stopped finally in 1941-2 which is the last date Craigleith appears in the Quarry List.[78] After the Second World War Craigleith quarry was gradually filled in. In 1992, Sainsbury's plc purchased the site and began work on a new superstore. The historical importance of the former Craigleith Quarry was brought to their attention and the upper, exposed section of strata has been proposed as a Regionally Important Geological Site (RIGS).

The best example of building in Craigleith liver rock was said to be seen in the south front of **Register House** [128] at the east end of Princes Street. As a result of his tests on various sandstones for use in Register House, Robert Adam reported in 1773 in favour of the tender of Messrs John Wilson and David Henderson, the Edinburgh masons, who were to use Craigleith or Ravelston stone, sand from Leith links and Gilmerton lime. Ravelston stone was included because experience of its use in Heriot's Hospital, some of which had stood for almost 150 years, showed 'that it will neither blow nor waste, and that it is free of sulphur and brown spotts'. Work on

Register House stopped during winter months, though stone was still being pre-pared, and the completed work was covered with straw. From 1778 work was stopped as the money ran out and the building stood empty and incomplete: 'the most mag-nificent pigeon house in Europe'. When work resumed on the dome in 1785 the pas-sages were to be paved with stone from Hailes which was to be used in conjunction with Craigleith for the gallery of the dome. This stage of the building was complete by 1789. Additional storage space to the north was added in the 1820s, again using Craigleith and pavement stone from Craigleith, Hailes and Carmyllie quarries (the lat-ter in the Lower Devonian *Dundee Formation* near Arbroath).[79] The lower part of the front of Register House, together with the whole of the rest of the walls are of broached ashlar. The upper parts of the front are of polished stone with the ground floor rusticat-ed. Cleaning of the exterior of the building in 1969 has resulted in the development of an orange tinge in the surface of the stone produced by the migration of iron oxide. Thus the building, while largely constructed of sandstone from Craigleith, does not have the appearance it would have had when freshly quarried.

Another building which has not been cleaned but shows the use of Craigleith stone at its grandest is the incomplete **National Monument** [140] on Calton Hill construction of which began in 1826. Here, the 12 columns (detail shown in Figure 2.8), each consisting of 13 pieces of sandstone, 'all laid on their natural bed' and 'spec-imens of the best common rock from this quarry'[80] are surmounted by an impressive architrave. The quality and colour of the best common rock was as good as liver rock. Poorer material from these regular strata which could be almost 3m (9 feet) thick was only fit for rubble work.

The **Dean Bridge** [77], completed in 1831, is a testament to the quality of Craigleith sandstone and the skills of the designer and masons. It is an elegant example of a 19th century masonry bridge which, without supplementary strengthening, carries the mod-ern traffic of one of the main roads into the city. The bridge, designed by Thomas Telford, the first president of The Institution of Civil Engineers, comprises four arches, each of 27.4m (90 feet), rising to a maximum height of 32.3m (106 feet) over the bed of the Water of Leith. The hollow construction of the arches permits regular internal inspection. Weathered stones were replaced in 1964 using indents of Craigleith stone recovered from the demolished Waterloo Bridge, London.

According to James Gowans, writing in *The Builder* in 1881, the tenement at the northern corner of **Randolph Cliff** [76] (1849-9) was 'a notable example, not only of the stone, but of what I consider the best masonry in the city'.[81]

Other good examples of the use of Craigleith stone include:

City Chambers [15] (1761), High Street

No. 8 Queens Street [172] (1770-1)

St Andrew's and St George's Parish Church [110] (1785), George Street.

West Register House [90] (1812) Formerly St George's Church.

Royal Scottish Academy [4] (1822-26), The Mound. With Cullalo stone.

National Gallery of Modern Art [156] (1825), Belford Road. Formerly John Watson's College.

Leith Town Hall (1827), Constitution Street.

St Stephen's Church [84] (1827-8), St.Vincent Street.

Maidencraig

West of Craigleith Quarry, within a stone's throw, is the site of Maidencraig Quarry, also known as Gibb's Quarry, and also working the *Craigleith Sandstone* which produced a very similar stone. The Maidencraig Quarry is first recorded as providing stone for **Edinburgh Castle** [9] during the latter months of 1628.[82] In June 1773 this quarry was providing stone for the North Bridge. By that date it was considered that enough stone had been quarried for work on the north abutment. Moreover, steps quarried for the stair up to the theatre which lay at the north end of the bridge were cluttering the quarry and getting in the way of the quarriers.[83] By 1775, the City Chamberlain was being authorised to pay for damage done to the Maidencraig by the City's quarriers.[84]

In the 'Articles and Conditions of Roup and Sale of the grounds of Drumsheugh' (1822), (i.e. Randolph Crescent, Ainslie Place and Moray Place) the Earl of Moray laid down what could be built in the 13 acres (5.3 hectares) which he feued. One of the quarries which he specified as providing suitable material was Maidencraig, (the others were Craigleith and Redhall), suggesting that it was working at that time.[85] The first Ordnance Survey map of that part of Edinburgh, published in 1853, shows that Maidencraig quarry was flooded, so that it is likely to have been abandoned by then. The quarry became a refuse tip in 1926 and has been completely filled in and recently redeveloped.

Barnton Park

The sandstone from this quarry is similar to that quarried at Craigleith just two miles (3km) to the east and was marketed as 'Craigleith Stone' and seems to have been regarded as a substitute when Craigleith stone became scarce.

PLATE 1 Edinburgh from Craigleith Quarry
Coloured lithograph by William Leighton Leitch (c.1854)
Reproduced by courtesy of Edinburgh City Libraries.

PLATE 2 Corncockle Quarry, Lochmaben
Early workings revealed abundant fossilised reptilian labyrinthodont footprints. This drawing by Sir William Jardine shows footprints preserved on an inclined bedding plane to the right of the flooded area.
Reproduced from *The Ichnology of Annandale* by Sir William Jardine (1853).

PLATE 3 George Square No.20 [43]: detail
An example of the use of local dolerite snecks (possibly from Salisbury Crags) with sandstone ashlar of the
Kinnesswood Formation (1775).
A A McMillan, 1998.

Plate 4 Old College, The University of Edinburgh [28]
Columns of the finest 'Liver rock' of Craigleith sandstone (1827).
A.A. McMillan, 1998.

Plate 5 Roseburn Primary School, Roseburn Street
'Pink' and 'blue', coursed squared rubble from Hailes with red Corsehill sandstone dressings (1893).
A A McMillan, 1998.

PLATE 6 National Gallery, The Mound [5]
An example of recently cleaned Binny sandstone used in the east wall (1859).
A A McMillan, 1998.

PLATE 7 Royal Scottish Academy, The Mound [4]
Here the grey sandstone from Craigleith (and Cullalo?) in the foreground contrasts with the warmer Binny
sandstone behind (1826).
A A McMillan, 1998.

PLATE 8 McEwan Hall, The University of Edinburgh [37]
Ashlar of Carboniferous sandstone from Polmaise Quarry, Stirlingshire and Prudham Quarry, Northumberland.
Note the red sandstone columns from Corsehill Quarry, Annan (1897).
A A McMillan, 1998.

PLATE 9 Former Scottish Equitable Assurance Building, North St David Street [116]
Purplish pink stone from Doddington, Northumberland was used to construct this building (1899). Contrast with
the red sandstone from Corsehill and Moat used for the National Portrait Gallery [114] (1890) (to the right).
A A McMillan, 1998.

PLATE 10 Saltire Court, Castle Terrace [63]
Buff sandstone from Stainton, Barnard Castle and red sandstone from Gatelawbridge (Newton Quarry), Thornhill (1991). BGS Photograph MNS5592A (1991)

PLATE 11 The Caledonian Hotel, West End [65]
Probably the best-known building constructed of Permian red sandstone from Locharbriggs and Corncockle quarries, Dumfries & Galloway (1903)
A.A.McMillan, 1998.

PLATES 12A AND 12B The Museum of Scotland, Chambers Street [27]
Hopeman Sandstone from Clashach Quarry, Elgin used in the rain screen cladding of the new museum (opened
by H.M. The Queen on 30 November 1998)
A.A.McMillan, 1998.

PLATES 13A AND 13B The Scottish Widows Fund and Life Assurance Society building, Morrison Street [163]
A fine use of the multi-coloured Hopeman Sandstone from Clashach Quarry, Elgin in the recently constructed
Scottish Widows building, Morrison Street (1997).
A.A.McMillan, 1998.

PLATE 14 Nos.1-3 York Place/ Paton Building façade [176]
This building was refaced in 1998 using Hopeman Sandstone from Clashach Quarry, Elgin.
By permission of Clark Stone Limited, Main Contractors on the Paton Building, York Place, Edinburgh.

The quarry produced three types of stone. The lowest bed of grey stone, the so called 'Craigleith', was used for building the Imperial Institute, London in 1880. Above this was the 'blue liver rock' a dark blue-grey stone used not only for building but also for polishing glass. The top bed was known as 'common rock', a light fawn coloured rock interspersed with dark carbonaceous markings. It was soft and the markings rendered it unsuitable for the 'second class structural work'. A black sand-stone was reputedly also worked.[86]

This quarry is not shown on maps of Edinburgh up to and including the first Ordnance Survey map (1853). Neither is it listed in the Mineral Statistics of 1858 which give details of active quarries in that year.[87] The first Quarries List (1895) notes that 18 men were working there. The work force rose to 30 in 1901 but although the quarry was still working in 1914, activity ceased before the end of the First World War.[88] Unlike so many of Edinburgh's quarries the working at Barnton Park has not been infilled, perhaps because it lies in the middle of Bruntsfield Golf Course. Although flooded, it remains very much as it must have been in 1914.

There is no known record of specific Edinburgh buildings built of stone from the quarry. Presumably the stone was used for housing in the Davidson's Mains area.

Ravelston

The old Ravelston Quarry, situated north of Ravelston House, together with that at Craigcrook to the west, are considered to have worked the *Craigleith Sandstone* and therefore the same bed of stone as at Craigleith Quarry. It was very similar to that from Craigleith being greyish-white, very fine grained and almost as hard.

The earliest surviving record of quarrying is found in the Town Council Records for the years 1511-2. Before the Reformation, the land belonged to the collegiate church of St Giles and the quarrying was let on behalf of the clerical official or prebender, one John Rynde, to Robert Cunningham, quarrier. Cunningham was allowed the first year rent-free, as he was required to clear the quarry. Later he had to pay £3 Scots annual rent and 'yearly a cow's grass' as well as providing stone for the Kirk and Town's works.[89] In the 1530s, Ravelston provided many loads of stone which were carried to **Holyrood** [146] for use in the construction of the Palace. The contemporary Accounts of the Masters of Works frequently mention payments for workmen 'putting down stones' for supplying ashlar, sill and lintel, great dressed stones for jambs of windows, flat stones, newels and pillar capitals. There were payments too, to blacksmiths who sharpened the quarrymen's picks. Finally Ravelston produced three great stones 'for sering of walter to the kichingis and twa gutteris to the samyn'.[90]

Ravelston quarries produced stones for the gutters of the roof of **St Giles Kirk** [18] in 1590.[91] The King's Master Mason, William Wallace, spent two days at Ravelston quarries in July 1625 at the winning of 'nine great stones for the king's badges' for the great hall in Stirling Castle.[92] By that time, the quarries were in the hands of the Foulis family. Three years later, the accounts of the Treasurer of Heriot's Hospital record the supply of double jambs and pillars at the commencement of building of the Hospital in Lauriston.[93] In July 1632, the Town Council began to take stone from Ravelston for **Parliament House** [21], appointing John Ronald, who had been quarrying at the Burgh Muir, and who was to be the chief quarrier of fine stone, to go out to Ravelston. Ronald was discharged temporarily by the Town Council in June 1635 when he objected to additional workers being sent from Society Quarry to Ravelston, perhaps in an attempt to step up production there. Transport costs were an important item in the building of Parliament House. Both sledges and carts were used. A double ashlar cost 10/- Scots at the quarry in December 1632 and 15/- Scots for carriage. Only one double ashlar could be carried in a cart and a single one on a sledge for which 10/- Scots carriage was charged.[94] To the south and east, old quarry roads can still be seen in the woods. The Parliament House was refaced with ashlar from Craigleith in 1807–10. By 1795, the quarries were owned by Mr Alexander Keith of Ravelston.[95] It seems that the Ravelston quarries did not survive the decline in building activity after the great boom of the mid–1820s because in 1845 it is recorded that they had been out of use for twenty years.[96] By then, however, one of the quarries in the vicinity had been drained and a tenant was being sought. It was reputed that the quarry flooded overnight about the year 1820; the quarrymen having tapped a subterranean spring. In 1960, the quarry was drained and subsequently filled although there is still a considerable amount of sandstone exposed, particularly in the old part of the quarry immediately to the east.

Although building stone was quarried at Ravelston for hundreds of years there are few good examples of its use in central Edinburgh; the best being the older work on the north side of **George Heriot's School** [33] which faces the Castle. Building began in 1628 with the construction of the north-west tower. There, the polished ashlar is grey and shows little sign of weathering. The mason's marks cut in the early 17th century can still be clearly seen. The front of the building, on the north side, was faced with Ravelston stone. Rubble from Craigmillar was used to face the other three sides. These were re-faced with Craigleith ashlar in 1833 after the entrance was transferred to the south side in 1828. It has been observed that the 'work is so skilfully executed that the alteration can be detected only by contrasting the cold hue of the Craigleith stone then used with the golden colour of the original stone quarried at Ravelston'.[97]

Craigcrook

This quarry, also known as Well Craig, Old Kenny, or Stevenson's quarry, lies to the east of Ravelston Quarry. It was also opened up in the *Craigleith Sandstone*. It remained flooded for many years and is now infilled.

Granton Quarries

The *Craigleith Sandstone* was worked at the northern end of the Granton Dome in several quarries, notably Granton Sea Quarry and Granton Land Quarry. Stone from Granton was described as hard and cream coloured.[98] The quarry at Granton Point was described as being second only in extent to Craigleith. The Mineral Statistics refer to Granton Point, Pennywell and Royston quarries.

Quarrying near Granton Point was undertaken at an early date. The earliest recorded use of stone is in the Accounts of the Master of Works in the work on **Holyrood Palace** [146] in 1532.[99] Small boats ferried some of this stone to Leith Sands from whence it was carted to Holyrood. Most, however, was carted all the way. Granton supplied ashlar, sills and lintels, paving and guttering, turnpike stair newels and pillars for 'upholding the gallery'. This early work carried on until 1536.

A few years later, in 1552-53, the accounts of the City Treasurer for the stonework at **Leith Bulwark**[100] show that stone was again being hewn and dressed at Granton and ferried to Leith. In 1553, half an ell of velvet was given to the Laird of Carrubber for permission to dig stones at Granton for one year.[101] In July 1555, payment was again made to the Laird for 'quarry leave' but inflation had raised the price to one ell of black velvet.[102] Knowledge of further development of quarries at Granton during succeeding centuries is patchy.

In 1835 a quarry, later known as Granton Sea Quarry, was opened to provide stone for **Granton Harbour** - the Duke of Buccleuch's 'magnificent enterprise'.[103] Victoria Jetty was opened three years later. By 1855 the west breakwater was complete and the east breakwater was nearly finished to make a 'capacious tidal harbour'.

By then, the quarry had expanded to 8 acres (3.2 hectares) and was 24m (80 feet) deep and 'only second in extent to the great quarry of Craigleith'.[104] It formed a headland with the north and west sides exposed to the waves. Although the supply of stone was nearly exhausted and a new quarry site nearby was being considered, work continued despite fears that the sea might break through. Between 3 and 4 am on the stormy morning of Friday 26th October 1855, near the high tide, a section of the west side of the quarry, 61m (200 feet) long by 24m (80 feet), collapsed allowing the sea to rush in, filling the quarry basin in 10 minutes. Fortunately because the collapse happened in the hours of darkness, none of the quarry's workforce of 50 to 60 men was present, but the foreman, Robert Muir, had a lucky escape as his house collapsed over 'the fatal precipice that yawned beneath'. One of the children had kept the family awake so that, when the front of the house began to topple, they were able to make a rapid escape by the back window. Almost all of the Muir family's belongings went into the sea along with a pumping engine and other valuable equipment. Much effort was unsuccessfully expended during 1856 to try to recover the quarry plant. Enough stone had been accumulated on the landward side of the quarry to satisfy immediate needs at the breakwater. Work on moving this stone had a tragic consequence when on 28th December 1855, a chain broke killing one of the workmen in the quarry.[105]

Quarrying on a modest scale continued during the latter part of the 19th century and into the 20th century. A quarry called Pennywell Parks, inland of Granton Point, was operational in 1895. It employed 18 men in 1900, but by 1904, it was not regularly used. Latterly, quarrying activity in the area is recorded only in 1925 when 12 men were employed in a quarry in the Royston area.[106] According to Craig, Granton stone was 'once extensively used for building' and possessed a good weathering property.[107]

Bearford's Quarries

These sandstone quarries were situated in Bearford's Parks which lay on the north side of the Nor Loch (site of today's Princes Street Gardens) and worked the *Craigleith Sandstone*. Bearford's Parks occupied ground stretching from near the West End of Princes Street to the present position of the Balmoral Hotel. Before the Reformation this land was part of the endowment of the Abbey of Holyrood.

The earliest mention of the quarries was in 1462, when stones were obtained to build **Trinity College Church** [133] at the instigation of Mary of Guelders, widow of James II of Scotland. The church was erected on the north side of what is now Waverley Station and, to judge from old engravings, it must have been a very imposing edifice.[108] It was considered to be, with the exception of Holyrood Abbey, the finest ecclesiastical building in Edinburgh at the time. When the North British Railway Company acquired the land, the church was destined for demolition and, despite strong objections, it was agreed in 1848 to raze the building. Many of the stones were preserved and numbered with a view to re-erection at some suitable location.[109] The stones lay on the southern slopes of the Calton Hill for about 30 years, before a decision was taken to rebuild the church in Jeffrey Street. Unfortunately many of the stones had disappeared and only the apse and adjoining part of the choir of the original building could be completed and incorporated in the new church which was finally opened in 1877.[110] This new church was partly demolished in 1964. Examination of the present structure in Chalmers Close will reveal that the stones are not in numerical order and some of the numbers are inverted! The building was closed in 1977 but had previously been used as a reading room annex to the Central Library, George IV Bridge.

At the beginning of the 18th century, Robert Hepburn of the Bearford estate (just west of Haddington, East Lothian), acquired 30 acres of green fields which lay between the Nor Loch (the site of today's East Princes Street Gardens) and a road called 'Lang Gait' or 'Lang Dykes'. The road, so-named because it was enclosed by two drystane dykes, was probably in line with the present Rose Street. The fields, stretching the whole length of the loch, became known as Lochbank or the Bearford's Parks, corrupted to Barefoots Parks. Hepburn appears to have been a difficult person. In December 1701 he got into trouble with the Town Council over 'encroachments' upon the Nor Loch. He was accused of throwing the rubbish from his quarry into the loch 'upon the other side of the North Loch, near the head thereof, opposite the Castle'. This indicates that quarrying had then extended some way westwards along the loch's north side.[111] In 1717 the Town Council bought the Parks from Hepburn.[112]

Pictures and maps of the mid 18th century show that extensive quarrying had, by then, been carried on over the east end of the Bearford's Parks (the present Waverley Market).[113] The first **North Bridge** was begun in 1763, and after many mishaps, was completed in 1772, thus opening the way for development of the New Town. It used stone quarried in the Bearford's Parks, supplemented with sandstone from Maidencraig Quarry. It seems likely that Bearford's quarries were worked for the first buildings in the New Town. William Jameson, mason, petitioned the Town Council to be allowed to quarry as much stone as he needed from the westernmost of the Bearford's Parks for a new house he was about to build in St Andrew Square in September 1770.[114] It appears likely that the oldest houses at the west end of the north side of **St Andrew Square** [115] are built of stone from Bearford's Parks. By 1786, it was apparent to the Superintendent of Public Works that further quarrying at the western part of Bearford's Parks was likely to interfere with the projected building in Princes Street, its cross streets and squares. He considered it necessary for the lines of the buildings to be set out so that any further quarrying could be confined to the street lines or to the clear ground on the south side of Princes Street.[115] It is not known whether any further quarrying did take place there after 1786.

As the line of Princes Street became established the workings disappeared under the upcast from the foundations of the buildings there and the creation of the Gardens. One of the quarries, 12m (40 feet) deep was rediscovered in the 1840s when the foundations for Sir Walter Scott's Monument were being laid. Consequently piles had to be driven to support the monument.[116] Excavations in1984 for the Waverley Market shopping complex re-exposed a yellowish white sandstone beneath quarry fill.

Upper Quarry Holes (London Road Quarries) and Lower (Nether) Quarry Holes

East of the Bearford's Parks, the *Craigleith Sandstone* was quarried from the earliest times in Upper Quarry Holes (London Road quarries) between the eastern end of Calton Hill and the northern end of Easter Road. To the north of these workings lay the Lower or Nether Quarry Holes (which probably worked the stratigraphically higher *Ravelston Sandstone*). Traces of the quarries of Upper Quarry Holes can be seen in the Royal Terrace Gardens, where there are mounds to which excavations from the construction of the houses in **Royal Terrace**, begun in 1821, may have contributed.

Situated in a lowly position outside the city walls, the Quarry Holes became a favourite location for duels and remained so until the mid 18th century. The quarries had often provided a convenient place for private discussion as was the case in 1557 when the earls of Arran and Huntly, with certain others of high rank, met to consider the activities of Mary of Guise, the Queen Regent, mother of Mary, Queen of Scots.[117]

During the civil war between the supporters of the boy-king James VI and those of his mother Mary Queen of Scots, a skirmish took place in June 1571, midway between Hawkhill and the Upper Quarry Holes. This day became known as 'Black Saturday' or 'Drury's Peace'. The Earl of Morton, one of the King's men, held Leith and marched to Hawkhill, provoking the Earl of Huntly and his men, who supported the Queen, to march from the Castle to meet him. Morton halted at the Quarry Holes and the English Ambassador, Sir William Drury, who had been with Morton on the previous night, went to the Quarry Holes and suggested to Huntly that a peaceful settlement was possible. Unfortunately, a fight broke out which was blamed on Drury who had to be protected from the Scottish mob.[118] Many years later, in 1650, guns were placed in the Quarry Holes, in an attempt to stem Oliver Cromwell's advance on Edinburgh.[119]

Towards the mid 17th century the land and quarries became the responsibility of Trinity Hospital. By 1700 they had become dangerous and several people had fallen into them with fatal results. The Treasurer of the Hospital was ordered to fill up the hollow ground in 1677.[120] However, he clearly failed to do so because it is recorded that an Englishman, Lt. Byron was drowned at the Nether Quarry Holes in 1691.[121] Further records indicate that the holes were left open until well into the 18th century. Robert Irvine was arrested and tried in the Broughton Tolbooth for a murder committed in April 1717. He was found guilty and condemned to be hanged on a piece of ground called 'the Green-side' in the vicinity of the quarries, after which his body was to be interred in the 'Quarry-hole near to the Tup Well'.[122] In 1736, James Colquhoun, merchant, and William Adam, architect, petitioned the Town Council to be allowed to quarry stone at the Nether Quarry Holes to build on two of their feus nearby.[123] It seems that the quarries were not filled in until 1766 when the City Treasurer was authorised 'to pay the Town's proportion of filling up the quarry at Nether Quarryholes'.[124] On the Calton Hill, William Jameson asked permission in 1761 to rent the quarry there for a few years.[125] The Town Council agreed to his working on the south side near to where he was building at the back of the Canongate. Daniel Murray and others got into trouble the same year for taking stone from the Calton Hill without permission from the Town Council.[126] Quarrying was still in progress as late as 1765 when a building for the Methodists near the head of Leith Street used Calton Hill stone.[127] It is not certain when these quarries finally closed.

The same sandstone was also quarried less than 400m ($^{1}/_{4}$ mile) to the east at Abbeyhill. Robert Milne, master mason, was ordered to fence his quarry next to the highway there in March 1692.[128]

Quarries in the West End of the New Town

Around the West End of the New Town *Craigleith Sandstone* has been extensively quarried though no trace remains of this activity. Some of the earliest work there began in 1616 when 'the new frie querrell be vest Sanct Cuthbertis' supplied stone for work on the Palace Block in **Edinburgh Castle** [9] and the Chapel in the south range of **Holyrood Palace** [146]. The Accounts of the Royal Master of Works refer to payments then for sharpening quarriers' tools and for water scoops, suggesting that this quarry was prone to flooding.[129]

Some quarries have been opened in strange places. In 1691, Henry Nisbet, one of the Nisbets of Dean, was allowed by the Kirk Session of St Cuthbert's Church to build a vault in the churchyard. Nisbet also sought permission to open a quarry there to provide the necessary stone. This was granted on condition that the quarry was filled in after completion of the building and that he paid a gratuity to the poor. Eventually a donation of £39 10/- Scots was extracted from Nisbet who was not only reprimanded for failing to fill in his quarry but was also reproved by the Kirk Session for drinking during divine service![130]

In the late 17th century, a quarry was dug near the Bakers' House which belonged to the Incorporation of Bakers on the south side of the Water of Leith, near the site of the present-day Miller Row at the Dean Bridge. The quarrying began to damage the road, so that it was 'impossible for ather man or horse to pass therby without the hazard of ther lyff'.[131] Frances Lowrie, a baillie of Portsburgh had to tidy rubbish dumped on the highway to the Water of Leith and level it up before he was to be allowed to quarry wall stones there.[132] In 1687 John Byers of Coats was in dispute over £400 Scots damages due to him by the Town Council and Incorporation of Bakers for their encroachment on his land in quarrying and building.[133] Not far away stone from the quarry at Drumsheugh only cost 2d cartage 'to neighbours and burgesses' but others paid 6d in October 1700.[134]

In November 1800, William Mutter was paid for damage caused to the land he was farming by quarrying on the lands of Coates near the West End of Princes Street.[135] This quarry is probably the one near Rothesay Place on Kirkwood's 1817 map.[136] Quarries in this area were still visible when the first Ordnance Survey map was published in 1853, although they were rapidly disappearing under new housing development.[137]

Broughton Quarries

In 1730 a number of Huguenot refugees came to Edinburgh from France, having fled the religious persecution which followed the revocation of the Edict of Nantes in 1685. These people, mainly silk weavers, were settled in a village, specially built for them in the area bounded approximately by the present Picardy Place, Broughton Street and parts of Forth Street, Hart Street and Union Street. The village which was built of stones from the Broughton quarries was called 'Picardie' after the French district from which most of the refugees came.[138] There is uncertainty about the nature of the stone from the Broughton quarries. Although this district is considered to be underlain by the *Craigleith Sandstone* the strata are cut by a thick dolerite dyke which was also worked.[139]

STONE FROM THE WEST LOTHIAN OIL-SHALE FORMATION

Ravelston No. 2 and Ravelston Black

The *Ravelston Sandstone* lies stratigraphically above the *Craigleith Sandstone* within the *Gullane Formation* (Table 3.1). It was worked mainly in quarries on Corstorphine Hill in western Edinburgh. Early quarrying of sandstones from this or a higher stratigraphical level may have taken place in and around Leith.

The *Ravelston Sandstone*, which attains a thickness of 38m, was worked in a line of three quarries lying to the north of, and stratigraphically below, the Corstorphine Hill dolerite sill. Ravelston No. 2 Quarry, also at one time known as Rosie's Quarry, produced greyish white, pale brownish buff and dark grey stone. The Ravelston Black Quarry got its name from the occurrence of a particularly black sandstone which may originally have been petroliferous. Oil trapped in pore spaces between sand grains in the rock may have been converted into a carbon residue when the dolerite sill was intruded.[140]

The quarries were still active and employing 16 men when the first Quarry List was published in 1895. At that time, the hard black rock found at the top of the westernmost Ravelston Black Quarry was sometimes used for glass cutting wheels. Stone continued to be taken from the Ravelston quarries until 1914, although the number of employees dwindled to five in 1909. Work began again after the First World War in 1920 when Ravelston No. 2 was operated by Thomas Lamb, builder,

Blackhall, employing 28 men. Between 1920 and 1939, Lamb built bungalows and villas in **Craigcrook Road** (including his own bungalow, 'Paramount', No.32) and at the top of **Gardiner Road, Blackhall**.[141, 142] Two quarries were working in 1922 but thereafter activity declined, with between nine and eighteen men employed until 1937. The last year that Ravelston appears in the Quarry List is 1939.[143]

Ravelston No.2 produced an excellent building and monumental stone for home and abroad. In western Ireland it was used in the Lusitania Memorial. Craig refers to Ravelston Quarry producing stone for villas at Trinity and it is presumed that the stone came from Ravelston No.2 rather than the old Ravelston Quarry.[144] Ravelston No. 2 also produced 'non-slipping' paving stones, e.g. at the top of Leith Walk.[145] In Edinburgh, notable examples of monuments build of stone from Ravelston No.2 quarry include:

Scottish American War Memorial [7] (1927). West Princes Street Gardens
Corstorphine Old Parish Church War Memorial (1919-23), Kirk Loan.

Leith Hill

This 'lost' quarry is mentioned in the Accounts of the Master of Works for the work done on **Holyrood Palace** [146] in 1529.[146] In August and September of that year the Accounts record payments to parties of quarriers and workmen at this quarry. So far as can be found, it is not mentioned again, and there is no sign of it on any map of the area. The first Ordnance Survey map published in 1853[147] shows Hillhousefield House, immediately to the south-west of the junction of Pitt and South Fort streets. It is possible that this refers to the hill where the quarry lay. If so, its stratigraphical position is at or above the level of the *Ravelston Sandstone*.

Wardie

Reference to a quarry, between Wardie House and the Forth, is made by Russell.[148] About 1657 General Monk gave orders to build a fort or citadel in Leith. The location is still called 'The Citadel', off Commercial Street. Buildings were demolished to provide the stone, but more was required, and was obtained from this quarry.

Hailes

In the *West Lothian Oil Shale Formation*, the *Hailes Sandstone* (Table 3.1) was worked in adjacent quarries at Hailes and Redhall on the south-western outskirts of the city.

However, the stone from the two localities is very different. Hailes Quarry (Figures 2.3, 3.7 and 3.8) produced a laminated stone of three colours, pink, blue-grey and white, while Redhall produced a massive unlaminated stone. Hailes and Redhall quarries lay either side of the Hailes Syncline, a fold with a NNE-SSW trending axis such that the strata dipped 10-15° eastwards at Hailes and 12-25° westwards at Redhall.

According to colour, the two varieties of stone produced at Hailes Quarry were known as 'Blue' (or 'Grey') Hailes and 'Pink' Hailes. Both are characterised by carbonaceous and micaceous ripple laminae and wispy partings (Figure 2.3). Silty partings are common. 'Pink' Hailes owes its pink tint to the presence of iron oxide. Irregular micaceous streaks, coloured deep red by iron oxide, are also present but the overall good weathering properties of the stone were unaffected. 'Blue' Hailes was largely used for stone steps in stairs and platts (slabs for stone landings in tenements), for rubble work and for foundations where great strength was required.

In 1882, the quarry was said to have been in operation for 300 years. The stone was interbedded with mudstone bands, the whole being described as 'smooth and level as if they had been dressed by hand'.[149] Now completely infilled, it formerly revealed the following section:[150]

Sandstone, with alternations of blaes	22m
Blaes	21m
'Pink' Hailes Sandstone	46m
'Blue' Hailes Sandstone	at least 9m

At the north end of the quarry, the blue stone was more of a liver rock in which lamination was not discernible. During the first half of this century the blaes (mudstones) on the east side of the quarry were worked for brick-making.

Hailes Quarry boasted a steam engine, set up in 1787 to pump out water[151] but this cannot have been entirely successful because in 1805 a large water-driven wheel was being used to drive a water pump to drain the quarry.[152] By 1845, the quarry was 27.4m (90 feet) deep. Despite the quarry's proximity to the Union Canal, most of the stone was carted to Edinburgh.[153] At the peak of production in 1825, 600 cartloads of stone were transported to the city at 3/- Sterling per load, 6d for the stone and 2/6d for cartage, but by 1845, it had been reduced to 60 to 70 cartloads per day.

By 1893, the quarry was exporting stone to London. In 1895, 139 men worked in the quarry. Over the next three decades the number of employees fluctuated with as many as 225 in 1899, with regular working continuing until 1914, and as few as

12 in 1928, by which time stone was only being worked intermittently. By 1931 only mudstone for brick-making was being regularly used. Extraction of mudstones continued until 1943-44, when Hailes appeared in the Quarry List for the last time.[154] At the time of maximum extent, Hailes Quarry excavations were undertaken both north and south of the Union Canal, with a tunnel connecting the two workings. A surviving plan of the quarry in the Scottish Record Office[155] shows it as it was in 1834 when there was a smithy and engine house at the north end. By the end of the 1970s there was hardly anything to show where this vast quarry had operated, having been completely filled in with rubbish. The site is now a public park.

George Smith, writing in 1835, described the use of the three kinds of Hailes stone: 'In the top feaks [strata] are found the strong hard flags which are extensively used for the foot-paths of the Edinburgh streets. The middle feaks are the finest, and used generally for stair-steps and plats, inside pavements, and chimney finishings. The under, or what is termed whin-feak, is used very extensively for ruble-work, and in this respect is not surpassed by any quarry in the country'.[156] The stone was unfit for polished ashlar. Hailes 'produced the best ruble stone of any quarry near Edinburgh' and it was emphasised that the stone 'should be placed horizontally in the building, otherwise the action of the weather causes them to separate, and peel off in flakes'. The beds were found of varying thickness, from five or six inches to three feet.[157]

According to James Gowans, a leaseholder of Redhall quarry (see below), Hailes 'owing to its laminated structure, is used greatly for foundations of buildings, plats, steps, etc'.[158] Apart from these products, the quarry yielded almost exclusively rubble stone, with the exception of a large mass of liver rock quarried c.1820 used to build the front of **Coates Crescent** [67].

The 'pink' and 'blue' stone, found near the base of the quarry, was used after the mid-19th century, in many public buildings. From 1872 onwards, it was used, particularly in the Edinburgh Board schools, as coursed or snecked rubble along with ashlar dressings around doors and windows employing red sandstone from Dumfries & Galloway. For example, **Roseburn Primary School**, (1893) Roseburn Street (Plate 5), is built of 'pink' and 'blue' Hailes with red Corsehill dressings. In the **Royal (Dick) School of Veterinary Studies** [46] (1909-16), Summerhall, 'pink' Hailes was used, together with purplish pink Doddington stone. Together with Binny and Carmyllie stone, 'blue' Hailes was used in the construction of the **New College & Assembly Hall** [12] (1845-50), Mound Place. Other examples of Hailes stone include:

Blue or Grey Hailes

Free Church of Scotland College [159], (1858-63), Mound Place.
Royal Infirmary [35] (1872-9), Lauriston Place.
Dalry Primary School [57] (1876-77), Dalry Road.
Leith Academy Secondary School Annex (1885-87). Formerly Lochend Road School, Lochend Road.
Sciennes Primary School [48] (1889), Sciennes Road.
Scotch Whisky Heritage Centre [10] (1896). Formerly Castlehill School, Castlehill, The Royal Mile. With Corncockle margins.

Pink Hailes

Cluny Gardens, No.1 (1880). Formerly 'Red House'. With quoins from Corsehill.
St Anne's Church, Corstorphine (1912), Kaimes Road. With ashlar from Cullalo.

Redhall

At Redhall Quarry, 500m to the east of Hailes Quarry, the stone was of quite a different character consisting of massive beds of unlaminated stone. Comparing the sandstone from Hailes Quarry with that from Redhall in Edinburgh's buildings, it is hard to believe that they belong to the same stratigraphical horizon. Carmichael (1837) pointed to the massiveness of the beds in the quarry and described them in these terms: 'This rock is of unknown depth, with about 200 yards [183m] of open front, upwards of 100 feet [30m] perpendicular in one solid mass, exclusive of 10 feet to 30 feet [3-9m] of tirring [overburden]: dip 20° north-west'.[159] Gowans (1881) considered sandstone from Redhall to be from the same beds as those at Craigleith for which there is a good match.[160]

Sandstone from Redhall, in contrast to that from Hailes, was much easier to work, especially when fresh, and was particularly suitable for delicate work. To some extent it replaced the very hard Craigleith stone towards the middle of the 19th century. Carmichael stated in 1837 that 'It is chiefly in mass, partly of a dull white and deep buff colour, termed liver stone, both of which are got in blocks of immense size'.[161] The stone long retained its polish. According to Craig the stone was of two colours 'one of which is red, containing a large percentage of iron, and the other white, but which gets discoloured when exposed to the atmosphere'.[162]

Redhall Quarry was first used in 1650 to build Redhall Castle. In 1757, Mr Inglis of Redhall advertised Redhall Quarry as the source of 1.5m (5 feet) diameter millstones in the *Edinburgh Courant*. Other quarries in the same area were advertised in 1764 and 1775. An advertisement in the *Edinburgh Advertiser* in 1781, drew attention to 'the excellent qualities of this stone both for hewn and ornamental work'.[163]

The stone was soft when dug out, making it easy to work. It soon hardened when exposed to the air.[164] Sometimes it contained silica nodules ('white whin' to the quarrymen) which could cause difficulties in working.[165] The quarry was still in the possession of the Inglis family in 1837 when 15 men were employed. The stone was loaded on to an inclined plane with cranes and thence transported to the Union Canal (opened in 1822) which conveniently passed through the middle of the quarry. A steam engine moved the wagons and kept the quarry clear of water.[166] Before 1821 a rent of £40 to £70 sterling per annum was paid. Under the management of George Johnston the rent jumped to £2,100 sterling per annum in 1824 and averaged £1,000 sterling per annum for a while. However, by 1832 Johnston was bankrupt, and although the Inglis family ran operations for some time, this arrangement was not successful and the quarry gradually fell out of use.[167]

In 1847, Walter Gowans took over the lease of the quarry, handing it over to his son James in 1850. James Gowans became a famous architect, Dean of Guild and the mastermind of the International Exhibition in the Meadows in 1886.[168] In 1851, a statue of Queen Victoria, carved by Handyside Ritchie from a block of Redhall freestone, was erected in front of Holyrood Palace at an estimated one-tenth of the cost of marble or bronze.[169] It was subsequently removed because the Prince Consort did not like it.

In 1857, James Gowans built Redhall Bank Cottages (now **8** and **10 Redhall Bank Road**) for his quarry workers.[170] These cottages demonstrate a cyclopean masonry style employing large stones of irregular form. In 1869 Redhall stone was one of those specified for frontages in the Warrender Estate, the other was Dunmore near Stirling.[171] Redhall Quarry was still being used in the 1870s. For example, **Tynecastle High School Annexe**, McLeod Street, built as Gorgie School, used Redhall stone in 1876.[172] In the early 1870s a second quarry, north of the old one, was opened. The main sandstone worked here was similar to, but softer than that in the older quarry and at Craigleith. It had the same 'bastard' or 'white whin' nodules. The main difference in the new quarry lay in the abundance and variety of plant fossils which were found there (Appendix 6). By 1895, workings at Redhall had closed.[173] Today the Redhall quarries on both sides of the canal have been largely filled in. One of them forms Redhall Park and here the mounds of 'tirr' can still be seen.

Stone from Redhall may be seen in several buildings in central Edinburgh although the detail and colour of many examples is obscured by more than one hundred years of grime. The former United Associated Synod Church in Lothian Road, now **Film House** [59] (1830-31) is one of the few buildings exhibiting stone from Redhall in anything like its original colour. The slight reddening in the stone may have been caused by the presence of oxides brought to the surface by cleaning in the late 1970s. The ashlar is polished and rusticated on the first floor level. Cracking can be seen in the V-sectioned chamfering of the rustication. Despite slight wear under the window sills, most of the detail is still very sharp after more than 150 years.

St John's Church [8] (1816-18), Princes Street, is built of polished ashlar with no bedding apparent and containing ironstone concretions like Craigleith. It has weathered well, although Craig[174] noted that stones set on edge had deteriorated. Other examples of the use of Redhall stone include:

St Paul's & St George's Episcopal Church, York Place [130] (1816-18)

Randolph Crescent, Nos. 15, 16 & 17 [75] (1820s)

STONE FROM THE LIMESTONE COAL AND UPPER LIMESTONE FORMATIONS

Joppa Quarries

Three quarries worked strata in the *Limestone Coal Formation* and *Upper Limestone Formation* (Table 3.1) at Joppa. One was situated at the shore where sandstone was obtained; a second quarry was opened about 1780. A third more extensive working called 'The Quarry' was bounded by the present Milton Road East, South Morton Street, the railway and Brunstane Road (now called Joppa Quarry Park). The *Joppa Sandstone* of the *Upper Limestone Formation* was worked for a yellow building stone. Hugh Miller, the Cromarty stone mason and famous geologist, was a frequent visitor to these quarries. The latter two quarries also exposed good seams of fireclay and before the end of the 18th century a large brickmaking works was established near the shore. At the peak of activity at the brickworks, 18,000 bricks were produced per week.[175]

Niddrie

At the west end of Newcraighall Road traces can be seen of another of Edinburgh's older quarries. This quarry worked building stone in the *Limestone Coal Formation* to the north the road. The nearby 'Quarry Cottages' were built about 1880, towards the end of the quarry's active life.[176] The earliest known use of stone from this quarry was in the building of part of **Holyrood Palace** [146] between 1529 and 1532. At that time Niddrie stone was used in the construction of chimneys, battlements, water spouts and lintels as well as for ashlar work.[177] By 1845 the 'excellent and valuable quarry at Niddry' was suspended except for estate use.[178] Thirteen years later it was again in use but had ceased operation by the time the first Quarry List was published in 1895.[179]

REFERENCES

1. Shepherd, T., *Views of Edinburgh*, 1829, p.36
2. Grant, J., *Old and New Edinburgh*, 1, London, Paris and New York: Cassell, Petter, Galpin and Co., 1880, p.27.
3. MacGregor, A.G., The mineral resources of the Lothians, *Geological Survey Wartime Pamphlet*, No.45, 1945, p.16.
4. Browne, M.A.E., Dean, M.T., Hall, I.H.S., McAdam, A.D., Monro, S.K. and Chisholm, J.I. A lithostratigraphical framework for the Carboniferous rocks of the Midland Valley, 1996. *British Geological Survey Technical Report WA/96/29.*
5. MacGregor, A.G., *op.cit.*, 1945, p.17.
6. Bryce, W.M., The Burgh Muir of Edinburgh from the Records, *The Book of the Old Edinburgh Club*, 10, 1918, p.240.
7. *Extracts from the Records of the Burgh of Edinburgh* (1528-1557), Edinburgh, 1871, p.193.
8. *ibid* (1589-1603), 1927, p.210.
9. Armet, H. and Harris, S., The Tower of Merchiston, *The Book of the Old Edinburgh Club*, 31, 1962, p.14-15.
10. Bryce, W.M., The Flodden Wall of Edinburgh, *The Book of the Old Edinburgh Club*, 2, 1909, p.69.
11. Extracts from the Records of the Burgh of Edinburgh (1528-1557), Edinburgh, 1871, p.312.
12. *ibid*, (1589-1603), 1927, p.210.
13. Hannay, R.K. and Watson, G.P., The building of Parliament House, *The Book of the Old Edinburgh Club*, 13, 1924, p.21.

14. *Extracts from the Records of the Burgh of Edinburgh*, (1642-1655), 1938, p.95.

15. Bryce, W.M., *op.cit.*, 1918, p.240.

16. *Extracts from the Records of the Burgh of Edinburgh*, (1689-1701), 1962, p.186.

17. *ibid*, (1689-1701), 1962, p.280.

18. Kirkwood, R., *Map of Edinburgh*, 1817.

19. Smith, C.J., *Historic South Edinburgh*, 1, p.50.

20. Bryce, W.M., *op.cit.*, 1918, p.29.

21. Taylor, A. On a section recently exposed at Marchmont Road. *Transactions of the Edinburgh Geological Society*, 1883-88, Vol 5, p.104.

22. Cant, M., *Marchmont in Edinburgh*, Edinburgh: J. Donald, Ltd., 1984, p.66-67.

23. Paton, H.M., (editor) *Accounts of the Masters of Works for building and repairing Royal Palaces and Castles*, 1, (1529-1615), p.138, 223.

24. *Extracts from the Records of the Burgh of Edinburgh* (1528-1557), 1871, p.302.

25. Hannay, R.K., and Watson, G.P.H., *op.cit.*, 1924, p.50.

26. *Accounts of the Masters of Works*, 2, (1616-1649), 1982, p.402, etc.

27. *Transactions of the Architectural Institute of Scotland*, 2, 1851-2, p.36.

28. *Statistical Account of Scotland*, 1, 1845, p.21.

29. Royal Commission on the Ancient Monuments of Scotland. *An inventory of the ancient and historical monuments of the City of Edinburgh*, 1951, p.212.

30. Craig, G., Building stones used in Edinburgh: their geological sources, relative durability and other characteristics, *Transactions of the Edinburgh Geological Society*, 6, 1893, p.257.

31. *List of Quarries under the Quarries Act*, 1901, 1902, 1906, 1908, 1914, 1937.

32. Macgregor, A.G. *op. cit.*, 1945, p.16.

33. *Accounts of the Masters of Works*, 1, (1529-1615), p.2, 71, 147, 151.

34. Gray, W.F., The quarrying of Salisbury Crags, *The Book of the Old Edinburgh Club*, 18, 1932, p.181.

35. *Extracts from the Records of the Burgh of Edinburgh* (1528-1557), Scottish Burgh Records Society, Edinburgh, 1871, p.42.

36. *ibid*, p.188.

37. *ibid*, (1573-1589), Edinburgh, 1882, p.411.

38. Bryce, W. M., *op. cit.*, 1918, p.239, 240.

39. Hannay, R.K. and Watson, G.P., *op. cit.*, 1924, p.21, 25, 31.

40. *Extracts from the Records of the Burgh of Edinburgh*, (1642-1655), Edinburgh, 1938, p.254.

41. *ibid*, (1573-1589), 1882, p.206.

42. *ibid*, (1665-1680), 1950, p.80.

43. Paton, H.M., Lands of St Leonards: Southern Section, *The Book of the Old Edinburgh Club*, 24, 1942, p.205.

44. Mitchell, G.H. and Mykura, W., The geology of the neighbourhood of Edinburgh, 3rd Edition, *Memoirs of the Geological Survey (Scotland)*, 1962, p.53.

45. *Edinburgh District 1:25 000 Geological Special Sheet, Parts of NT16,17,26,27 and 37*. Classical Areas of British Geology, Institute of Geological Sciences, 1971.

46. Smith, G., Account of the quarries of sandstone in the Edinburgh and Glasgow districts, and of the principal slate quarries in Scotland, *Prize Essays and Transactions of the Highland and Agricultural Society of Scotland, (New Series)*, 4, 1835, p.81-82.

47. Craig, G., *op.cit.*, 1893, p.255-259

48. MacGregor, A.G., *op. cit.*, 1945, p.17

49. Smith, G., *op. cit.*, 1835, p.83.

50. Hull, E., *A treatise on the building and ornamental stones of Great Britain and foreign countries*, London: MacMillan, 1872, p.305

51. Notes on a visit to Craigleith Quarry in 1938 by E.M. Anderson. *Archives of the British Geological Survey, Edinburgh*. (The date at which the height of the old quarry face was said to have been 110m is uncertain.)

52. *Accounts of the Masters of Works*, 1, p.353.

53. *ibid.*, 2, p. 6, 7, 14, 17, 56.

54. Smith, G., *op. cit.*, 1835, p.81-82

55. *Scots Magazine*, 53, 1791, p.149.

56. Craig, G., *op. cit.*, 1893, p.256.

57. Smith, G., *op. cit.*, 1835, p.81.

58. Shepherd, T., *op. cit.*, 1829, p.36.

59. Smith, G., *op. cit.*, 1835, p.83.

60. Forsyth, R., *Beauties of Scotland*, 1, 1805, p.279.

61. *The Builder*, 1848, p.349.

62. Masson, D., *Memories of two cities* (papers from Macmillan's Magazine, 1864-65), Edinburgh, 1911, p.22.

63. Craig, G., *op. cit.*, 1893, p.255.

64. Smith, G., *op. cit.*, 1835, p.83.

65. *Extracts from the Records of the Burgh of Edinburgh*, 1805, p.224.

66. *ibid.*, p.315.

67. *ibid.*, p.343.

68. Mears, F.C. and Russell, J., The New Town of Edinburgh, *The Book of the Old Edinburgh Club*, 23, 1940, p.33.

69. *The Builder*, August 11, 1845.

70. Bremner, D., *The industries of Scotland*, Adam & Charles Black, 1869, p.412.

71. *The Builder*, 1852, p.657.

72. Wilson, G., *Transactions of the Architectural Institute of Scotland*, 4, 1854-5, p.8.

73. Craig, G., *op. cit.*, 1893, p.257.

74. Brown, C., The occurrence of Gasteropods (*Platyostomella Scotoburdigalensis*) in a Lepidodendron from Craigleith Quarry, Edinburgh, *Transactions of the Edinburgh Geological Society*, 7, 1899, p.244.

75. *List of Quarries under the Quarries Act*, 1895, 1900, 1905.

76. *Minutes of Evidence taken before the Royal Commission on Metalliferous Mines and Quarries*, 2, 1914, HMSO.

77. Mackie, A., *Year Book, Royal Society of Edinburgh*, 1978, p.13.

78. *List of Quarries under the Quarries Act*, 1941-2.

79. Paton, H.M., The General Register House, *The Book of the Old Edinburgh Club*, 1930, 17, p.161,168

80. Smith, G., *op. cit.*, 1835, p.82

81. Gowans, Sir J., Building stones of Scotland. *The Builder*, 41, 1881, p.673

82. *Accounts of the Masters of Works*, 2, p.211-2.

83. *Town Council Records*, 90, (1773), p.244.

84. *ibid.*, 93, (1775), p.173.

85. Youngson, A.J., *The making of classical Edinburgh*, Edinburgh: Edinburgh University Press, 1966, p.218.

86. Watson, J.W., *British and foreign building stones*, Cambridge University Press, 1911, p.123.

87. Hunt, R., Mining Records, Mineral Statistics, part 2 (1858), *Memoir of the Geological Survey*, Longman and Co., 1860.

88. *List of Quarries under the Quarries Act*, 1895, 1901, 1914.

89. Extracts from the Records of the Burgh of Edinburgh, (1403-1528), Edinburgh, 1869, p.136.

90. *Accounts of the Masters of Works*, 1, (1529-1615), p.2, 223.

91. *Extracts from the Records of the Burgh of Edinburgh*, (1589-1603), p.19.

92. *Accounts of the Masters of Works*, 2, (1616-1649),p.170.

93. *Transactions of the Architectural Institute of Scotland*, 2, (1851-52), p.36.

94. Hannay, R.K., and Watson, G.P.H., *op. cit.*, 1924, p.21, 24,40.

95. *Statistical Account of Scotland*, 14, 1795, p.448.

96. *ibid.*, 1845, 1, p.207.

97. Royal Commission on the Ancient Monuments of Scotland, *op. cit.*, p.111.

98. Craig, G., *op. cit.*, 1893, p.258-259

99. *Accounts of the Masters of Works*, 1, p.82.

100. *Extracts from the Records of the Burgh of Edinburgh* (1528-1557), Edinburgh, 1871, p.278.

101. *ibid.*, (1528-1557) p.279.

102. *ibid.*, (1528-1557) p.312.

103. *Edinburgh Courant*, October 27, 1855.

104. Craig, G., *op. cit.*, 1893, p.258.

105. *Edinburgh Courant*, December 29, 1855.

106. *List of Quarries under the Quarries Act*, 1901, 1905, 1927.

107. Craig, G., *op. cit.* p.258.

108. Billings, R.W., *Baronial and Ecclesiastical Antiquities*, 1847, 2.

109. Geddie, J., The sculptured stones of the 'Royal Mile', *The Book of the Old Edinburgh Club*, 15, 1927, p.127.

110. Gray, W.F., *The Scotsman*, May 15, 1948.

111. *Extracts from the Records of the Burgh of Edinburgh* (1689-1701), 1962, p.295.

112. *ibid.*, (1701-1718), 1967, p.333.

113. Youngson, A.J., *op. cit.*, 1966, p.17-18 (illustration).

114. *Council Record*, 87, (1770), p.174-5.

115. *ibid.*, 108, (1786), p.271-2.

116. Grant, J., *Old and New Edinburgh*, 1, Cassell, Petter, Galpin and Co., 1880, p.303.

117. *ibid.*, 2, p.101.

118. *ibid.*, 3, p.133.

119. *ibid.*, p.151.

120. Extracts from the Records of the Burgh of Edinburgh (1665-1680), 1950, p.298.

121. *ibid.*, (1689-1701), p.64.

122. Fairley, J.A., The Old Tolbooth, *The Book of the Old Edinburgh Club*, 4, 1912, p.92.

123. *Council Record*, 57, (1736), p.18-19.

124. *ibid.*, 82, (1766), p.33.

125. *ibid.*, 76, (1761), p.259.

126. *ibid.*, 76, (1761), p.274.

127. *ibid.*, 81, (1765), p.30.

128. Billings, R.W., *op. cit.*, 1847, 2.

129. Imrie, J., and Dunbar, J.G., (editors) *Accounts of the Masters of Works*, 2, (1616-1649), HMSO., 1982, p.3,9,13,14.

130. Geddie, J., Sculptured stones of old Edinburgh: the Dean Group. *The Book of the Old Edinburgh Club*, 1, 1908, p.117.

131. *Extracts from the Records of the Burgh of Edinburgh* (1665-1680), 1950, p.166.

132. *ibid.*, p.319

133. *ibid.*, (1681-1688), 1954, p.212.

134. *ibid.*, (1689-1701), 1962, p.271.

135. *ibid.*, (1800), p.134.

136. Kirkwood, R., *op. cit.*, 1817

137. *Ordnance Survey 6-Inch Sheet Edinburgh*, 2 , 1853.

138. Grant, J., *Old and New Edinburgh*, 2, 1880, p.186.

139. Jameson, R., Geognostical description of the neighbourhood of Edinburgh, Part 1, *Edinburgh Philosophical Journal*, 1, 1819, p.352-363.

140. Tait, D., The occurrence of petroliferous sandstones in the Carboniferous rocks of Scotland and their relation to certain black sandstones, *Transactions of the Edinburgh Geological Society*, 12, 1932, p.90-104.

141. McArthur, M., *Bonnie Blackhall: From quarriers' village to garden suburb*. Edinburgh: Roxburgh Publications, 1995, p.20.

142. British Geological Survey Archives, *Ref. EE5602*.

143. *List of Quarries under the Quarries Act, 1939*.

144. Craig, G., *op. cit.* p.257.

145. British Geological Survey Archives, *op. cit.*.

146. *Accounts of the Masters of Works*, 1, p.82.

147. *Ordnance Survey Map Edinburgh*, 2, 1853.

148. Russell, J., Bonnington: its lands and mansions *The Book of the Old Edinburgh Club*, 19, 1933, p.183.

149. *The Builder*, 1882, p.624.

150. *Six inches to One Mile Geological Sheet NT27SW*, British Geological Survey, 1965

151. *New Statistical Account of Scotland*, 1, 1845, p.124.

152. Forsyth, R., *op. cit.*, 1, 1805, p.279.

153. Bremner, D., *op. cit.*, 1869, p.412.

154. *List of Quarries under the Quarries Act*, 1895, 1899, 1914, 1928, 1931, 1943-44.

155. Plan of Hailes Quarry shewing the face of rock excavated, 1834, RHP 3704

156. Smith, G., *op. cit.*, 1835 p.89.

157. *ibid.*, p.88–89.

158. Gowans, Sir J., 1881, *op. cit.* p.673.

159. Carmichael, J., An account of the principal marble, slate, sandstone and greenstone quarries in Scotland, *Prize Essays and Transactions of the Highland and Agricultural Society of Scotland (New Series)*, 5, 1837, p.405.

160. Gowans, Sir J., *op. cit.*, 1881, p.673.

161. Carmichael, J., *op. cit.*, 1837, p.406.

162. Craig, G. *op. cit.* p.259.

163. Inglis, J.A., *The Family of Inglis of Auchindinny and Redhall*, 1914, p.102-3, 191.

164. Carmichael, J. *op. cit.*, 1837, p.412.

165. Bremner, D., *op. cit.*, 1869, p.412.

166. Inglis, J.A., *op. cit.*, 1914.

167. *ibid.*

168. Smith, C.J., *op. cit.*, 1979, p.101.

169. *The Builder*, 1851, p.689.

170. McAra, D., Sir James Gowans, *Scottish Arts Review*, 13, 1972, p.25.

171. Cant, M., *op. cit.*, 1984, p.66-67.

172. Craig, G., *op. cit.*, 1893, p.259.

173. *List of Quarries under the Quarries Act*, 1895.

174. Craig, G. *op. cit.*, 1893, p.259.

175. Maclean, W.A., *St Philip's Joppa Parish Church*, 1976, p.13.

176. Gifford, J., McWilliam, C., Walker, D., *The buildings of Scotland, Edinburgh*. London: Penguin Books, 1984, p.546.

177. Accounts of the Masters of Works, 1, p.85, 88.

178. *Statistical Account of Scotland*, 1, 1845, p.21.

179. *List of Quarries under the Quarries Act*, 1895.

CHAPTER 8 | WHERE TO SEE SANDSTONES IN EDINBURGH'S BUILDINGS: PART 2. SCOTTISH AND ENGLISH QUARRIES AND THEIR BUILDING STONE PRODUCTS

"With railways interspersing the country, he [the architect] is not tied down to any particular stone or material, but may adopt that which he finds best suited for his purpose"

JAMES GOWANS, 1881[1]

During the 19th century the increasing demand for good quality building stone coupled with declining local resources, encouraged the use of stone from other parts of Britain. This chapter describes some of the main sources of sandstone from Scotland and England including some of the currently working quarries which are supplying material both for restoration and new build.

STONE FROM THE DEVONIAN OF ANGUS AND CAITHNESS

Carmyllie and Leoch

Flaggy sandstones of the *Dundee Formation* were extensively worked for paving stones at Carmyllie quarries, near Arbroath.[2] These quarries supplied stone for the paving and steps of **New College & Assembly Hall** [12] (1845-50), the **Bank of Scotland** [13] (1864-70) on the Mound and **Register House** [128] (1774-1834). On account of strength characteristics, stone from Carmyllie was used for engineering work, for example in the building of the piers of the Forth Railway Bridge in 1885.[3] Stone, described as 'bluish grey rather fine-grained sandstone or 'liver rock' from Leoch Quarry, north-west of Dundee, was also used in the city.[4] Together with stone from Darney, West Woodburn, it was used in the construction of the **Usher Hall** [64](1910-14), Lothian Road. Examples of stone from Leoch and Myreton can be seen in the **Meadows Pillars** [158] (Figure 6.2).

Caithness

The fine grain size and regular bedding of the grey, laminated Caithness flagstones makes them excellent materials for paving and roofing (Figure 3.3). Because of their high strength, thin slabs of very large length and breadth have been used for pavement. Notable examples of the use of flagstones, both for pavements and kitchen flooring, may still be seen in the Old Town. Many houses in Leith and older parts of Edinburgh were roofed with stone from the Scrabster quarries as well as from those of Carmyllie (see above).[5] Currently (1997),[6] flagstones are worked both for the home market and for export at several quarries including Spittal Quarry No.1, Watten (by A and D Sutherland), Spittal No.2 and Stonegunn, Castletown (by Caithness Stone Ltd.) and Weydale (by Caithness Flagstones Ltd.) south of Thurso. In Edinburgh, recent examples of the use of Caithness flagstone for pavement include the **Royal**

Mile development, **Holyrood Palace** [146] and **Festival Square**, east of the **Sheraton Hotel** [61], Lothian Road.

STONE FROM THE CARBONIFEROUS OF WEST LOTHIAN

The *Binny Sandstone* of the *West Lothian Oil-Shale Formation* (Figure 3.4) was extensively worked in West Lothian and Midlothian.[7, 8] The completion of the Union Canal in 1822 allowed stone from West Lothian, particularly from Binny and Humbie quarries, to be transported more economically to Edinburgh. This coincided with a declining production of the harder-to-dress Craigleith and Ravelston stone. The canal trade declined with the growth of the railways from 1842 onwards. The *Binny Sandstone* varies in thickness from about 76 to 152m and consists of several beds separated by shales. In the Broxburn district it is 107m thick. The stone is usually grey with rusty tints. At Craigton and White quarries the rock is white.

Binny

Binny Sandstone was first worked at Binny where several quarries supplied freestone for many of the finest buildings in Edinburgh during the 19th century.

Forsyth[9] (1846) gave the section in East Binny Quarry as:

Surface clay	9 feet [3m]
Shale	31 feet [9m]
Hard sandstone	3 feet [1m]
Good stone	26 feet [8m]

The strata dip 15° to the west. The upper seams of the working bed have a slightly greyish colour, the lower and by far the greater part is of a fine white colour. All the sandstone exposed at present is pale yellowish brown.

The sandstone at Binny contained bitumen which gave the rock a freckled appearance and according to Bremner (1869), 'wherever this is most distinctly marked, the stone is most durable'.[10] The bitumen is a hydrocarbon (ozokerite) which appears in joints or cavities. In 1850 Gowans collected some of this material from fissures in the rock at Binny Quarry and made it into black candles which were exhibited at the Great Exhibition in 1851. Gowans also noted that the 'best fakes are saturated with bitumen'.[11] At Binny and Humbie quarries and also Straiton Quarry (east of the Pentlands) the *Binny Sandstone* contains traces of oil. The stone at Straiton, although otherwise excellent, was stained with crude oil and this was found to mar the surfaces of the dressed stone and eventually led to the abandonment of the quarry.[12] Tait noted that the replacement of water by small amounts of oil in the pores between grains contributed to the durability of the stone.[13] He also mentions the disfigurement of the **Scott Monument** [3] (1840-46), **National Gallery** [5] (1850-59) and **Royal Scottish Academy** [4] (1831-36), by black patches on the surface of the stone, generally attributed to smoke pollution. He stated that 'close inspection of the distribution and shape of sooty patches and bands coupled with the knowledge that the rock does contain oil suggests the conclusion that the darker markings are oily patches to which cling a special thick coating of soot'.

By 1845, Binny appears to have superseded Craigleith stone. It was described as 'very nice material, probably not quite so durable as Craigleith but less costly to work and of better colour; for ornamental carving it is particularly good'.[14]

At Binny Quarry, freshly worked sandstone was grey but recently cleaned buildings exhibit an orange-coloured stone, e.g. **The National Gallery** [5] (Plate 6), **Royal Scottish Academy** [4] and **Bank of Scotland** [13] (1802-06) on the Mound and the **Dome Bar** [103] (formerly the Royal Bank of Scotland's 'temple') (1843-47) at 14 George Street. The Royal Scottish Academy also used stone from Craigleith and Cullalo (see below) which contrasts with the orange-brown stone from Binny and Humbie quarries (Plate 7). The stone seen in these buildings is little weathered although there is some scaling on the architrave on the east side of the central portico of the National Gallery. The stone in the latter is very uniform with a polished or lightly stugged finish. A different sandstone has been used for one of the shallow pilasters and in a few other places on the west side. These stones are probably replacements. Two nearby buildings where Binny stone has not been cleaned are the **Tolbooth St John's Church** [11] (1842-44) and the **New College & Assembly Hall** [12]. Both are heavily grimed but locally there is considerable scaling, for example, on the north side of the Tolbooth Church and around the north entrance to New College where the brownish yellow sandstone is revealed on worn buttresses. A single block of Binny stone, weighing about 20 tons when it left the quarry, was sculpted by John Steell into the **Queen Victoria Statue** and erected at the **Royal Scottish Academy** [4] in 1844.

A former fine example of the dark brown-tinted Binny stone was that used in the Life Association of Scotland building (1855) in Princes Street demolished in 1968.

A new quarry at Binny was re-opened temporarily in 1997 by the Stirling Stone

Group to provide replacement stone for repairing the **Scott Monument** [3]. A sufficient number of blocks were recovered before the quarry was filled in. Other buildings in which the use of Binny stone can be seen to good effect include:

City Observatory [138] (1818), Calton Hill

Donaldson's School for the Deaf [73] (1841-51), West Coates. Brown tint.

Daniel Stewarts and Melville College [80] (1849-55), Queensferry Road

Holyrood House Fountain [146] (1858-9)

Former General Post Office [132] (1866), East End, Princes Street

Hermand

At Hermand, West Calder, a 27m thick sandstone at the same stratigraphical horizon as Binny was formerly quarried. This stone has an overall grey appearance but is characterised by brownish laminations and reddish staining streaks or patches.

The weathering properties of this stone are variable. At the cleaned **Bank of Scotland** [106] (1885), 103 George Street, the stone has stood very well. Here it is polished throughout with rustication up to first floor level. Cross-bedding picked out by the darker laminations shows up throughout the front of the building. At the west wing of the **Royal Museum of Scotland** [27] (1885-89) in Chambers Street where there has been partial cleaning, the stone has not stood nearly so well, having had to be extensively replaced by stone indents from Stainton, County Durham, on sill courses and elsewhere. At the **Meadows Pillars** [158][15] (Figure 6.2), bedding is picked out by differential weathering on the polished faces of the Hermand sample though the stugged faces are not so weathered. Other notable uses of Hermand stone are:

St Mary's Cathedral School [69] (1885), Palmerston Place.

Calton Gaol [134] (1886), Calton Road.

Mercat Cross [19] (1885), High Street. Restoration.

Dalmeny

At Dalmeny Quarry, the *Binny Sandstone* is found in massive beds separated by partings of mudstone and siltstone. The quarry was worked 1874 to 1888 and transported to Edinburgh by railway. The light grey, slightly micaceous sandstone from Dalmeny is very similar to that from Binny Quarry but does not seem to have stood so well. By the 1890s stone was practically worked out.[16] The long polished ashlar front of the former **Bank of Scotland** [101] (1874-76), 62-66 George Street has stood quite well although there are signs of weathering on the ionic columns and on the balustrade in front. According to Craig (1893),[17] in the 1870s Dalmeny stone was extensively used in Drumsheugh, the east side of **Coates Gardens** [71] and **Magdala Crescent** [72] and neighbouring streets. On the east side of **Palmerston Place** (1880s) the polished front of **nos. 15-21** [68] has had to be repaired using sandstone from Stancliffe Quarry, Darley Dale in Derbyshire in 1985. Dalmeny stone was said to be weathering badly at the **Meadows Pillars** [158] (Figure 6.2) in 1888 but has not deteriorated much since then. Other uses include:

Great Junction Street tenements nos. 69 & 71 (1884).

Royal Overseas League [96] (1879-80), 100 Princes Street. Formerly Windsor Hotel.

Humbie

Humbie Quarry, north of Kirkliston, produced three colours of stone: white, grey and light brown. The sandstone has a freckled appearance in parts. Smith (1835) noted that the stone 'is very little laminated' and is 'almost entirely composed of granular concretions of white and grey translucent quartz, intermixed with scales of white mica and grains of feldspar'.[18] The quarry was abandoned by 1868 being unable to compete with other quarries.[19]

The white stone was most highly regarded and was used for the front part and portico of **Surgeon's Hall** [38] (1829-32), Nicolson Street, and for the **Robert Burns Monument** [142] and **Dugald Stewart Monument** [137] on Calton Hill. The grey stone was used for dressings of rubble buildings and for stair steps and plats.[20] According to Bremner, the stone was used in 'street buildings, especially in the Newington district'.[21] Other examples are the **Tron Kirk Steeple** [25] (1828) which was largely refaced with Darney stone in 1974-76 and the newer work for the **Royal Scottish Academy** [4] (1831-36).

Craigton

The quarry is situated between Winchburgh and Philpstoun and was opened up in the *Binny Sandstone*. In 1892 the quarry had recently been re-opened and the white stone occurred in a great massive bed with few shaly partings. The stone was used for the additions to **Surgeon's Hall** [38] (1890), Nicolson Street, and additions to **Craigcrook Castle** (1891), Craigcrook Road.[22]

STONE FROM THE CARBONIFEROUS OF FIFE

Fife sandstone from Longannet, Cullalo, Grange and Fordell was shipped across the Forth to Leith. More quarries were brought into use by the Edinburgh builders exploiting the new railways and transport was made easier with the opening of the Forth Bridge in 1890.

Much of the sandstone from Fife used in Edinburgh comes from the *Grange Sandstone* in the *West Lothian Oil-Shale Formation* (Figure 3.4). It has been worked principally at Grange, Newbigging and Dalachy quarries near Burntisland. Cullalo quarries may have worked this or a sandstone higher in the sequence. At Fordell, the quarry referred to as Millstonemeadow by Watson (1911)[23] is in strata of the *Lower Limestone Formation*.

Grange

At Grange Quarry the sandstone is at least 36m thick of which the basal 21m has been described as an excellent liver rock. Above this are 8m of sandstone beds which are only suitable for rubble work.[24] It has been described as a 'very pure greyish white sandstone' which hardens on exposure. Gowans stated that it was used particularly in Leith from 1870 onwards.[25] Examples of stone from Grange Quarry include:

Victoria Primary School (1875-1896), Newhaven Main Street.

Old College, University of Edinburgh, dome [28] (1887), South Bridge.

Seafield Lodge, Seafield Cemetery (1889), Seafield Place.

Bonnington Primary School (1875), Bonnington Road.

Newbigging

Newbigging Quarry previously exposed about 37m of strata. The bottom part of the sandstone is limy and passes down into hard limy siltstones and sandstones which rest on 5m of the *Burdiehouse Limestone*.[26] The latter has also been quarried and mined at this locality. In 1870, the quarry provided stone for the building of the Gustavi Cathedral in Gothenburg and was reopened by Scottish Natural Stones Ltd. in 1979 to provide stone for the repairs. The quarry was again reopened on 11 June 1984 to provide stone for the National Library of Scotland extension when only the bottom bed of the quarry was worked; the top beds were discarded as being not to specification.

The stone has been used at the new **National Library of Scotland Causewayside building** [47] (1984-87) & **Phase II** (completed 1994). The stone here is a very striking cross-bedded, light creamy brown, medium-grained sandstone with brown ferruginous spots. It has an attractive marbled appearance due to the presence of blotches of limonite. The stone is soft when quarried but is said to harden when exposed to the air. This is a stone without a proven reputation as it has not stood long enough to have its weathering qualities tested. However, in Burntisland, it has been used since the 1850s and is said to have weathered well.

Cullalo

The yellowish grey sandstone of the Cullalo quarries has been more widely used than the sandstone quarried at Grange or Newbigging. There were two main quarries and several smaller workings at Cullalo. The quarries had long lain abandoned until they were re-opened by Bryce in about 1864 for the building of **Fettes College** [81] (1864-70). In the early 19th century Cullalo stone had a high reputation though it was not as hard as the stone from Craigleith. It could be dressed easily when fresh but soon hardened on exposure. Gowans (1881) considered the stone to be durable, but owing to the expense of quarrying and difficulty of dressing, it had not continued in use.[27]

The greater part of the **High Kirk of St Giles** [18], apart from the medieval tower and 19th century additions, were encased between 1829 and 1833 with Cullalo stone. The sandstone which is mostly polished or lightly tooled, is greyish, fine-grained and slightly micaceous. The stone has been laid with the bedding mostly horizontal. Some stones exhibit cross-bedding. There is little evidence of weathering although some ironstone concretions are weathering out. At the foot of the Mound, recently cleaned Cullalo stone can be seen in the northern part of the western colonnade of the **Royal Scottish Academy** (1822-26) [4]. Here, comparisons may be made with Craigleith Sandstone which has a wispy appearance in some blocks and also with the slightly darker *Binny Sandstone* from Humbie and Binny quarries in West Lothian which are used for the rest of the colonnade (Plate 7). Other buildings which have used stone from the Cullalo quarries include:

Melville Pillar [117] (1820-23) St Andrew Square.

St Mary's Cathedral [69] (1874-1917), Palmerston Place.

Chapel of the Knights of the Thistle, St Giles Cathedral [18] (1909-11), High Street.

Lady Glenorchy's Church [182] (1908-10 & 1912-13), Roxburgh Place.

Elsie Inglis Nursing Home [147] (1923), Spring Gardens.

George Watson's College War Memorial (1920), Colinton Road.

Clunevar

Clunevar Quarry, west of Dunfermline, yielded sandstone from the *Limestone Coal Formation*. The building stone was described by Craig as a soft white sandstone.[28] It has been used in the building of the following tenements:

38 Marchmont Crescent [50] (1881).

Roseburn Terrace tenements (1882).

North Junction Street (1891).

Fordell

This quarry was situated near Aberdour and according to Craig, the stone was white when delivered but turned black in about a year. It was used in the building of **Old Granton Parish Church** (1877).[29]

STONE FROM THE CARBONIFEROUS OF THE STIRLING AND GLASGOW AREAS

With depletion of stone from quarries in the vicinity of Edinburgh, the more easily worked stone from Stirlingshire quarries and those further west near Glasgow were brought to Edinburgh by the newly opened railways, particularly from the 1860s onwards.

Bishopbriggs Quarries: Kenmure and Huntershill

The *Bishopbriggs* or *Kenmure Sandstone* of the *Upper Limestone Formation* was quarried and mined[30] at Bishopbriggs in Huntershill Quarry (Figure 3.9) where it is developed as two units, the lower 18m thick and the upper part 14m[31], separated by 3m of marine fossiliferous strata. Locally, the *Bishopbriggs Sandstone* is defined as lying below the *Huntershill Cement Limestone.*[32] The latter unit is, however, not always present elsewhere which makes the estimation of thickness of the *Bishopbriggs Sandstone* difficult. In general the sandstone is mainly fine- to medium-grained (in contrast to the coarse-grained pebbly *Barrhead Grit* which lies above the *Huntershill Cement Limestone* in Glasgow).

The *Bishopbriggs Sandstone* was worked at several quarries, especially at Huntershill and Robroyston, north of Glasgow. Kenmure was one of the Bishopbriggs quarries that supplied the stone used extensively in **Cockburn Street** [16], between 1859 and 1864, to give access to Waverley Station from the south. In 1987 many of the buildings showed signs of severe weathering. Since then much of the badly worn detail and scaling stonework, including that on the former **Old Cockburn Hotel** at the north end of the street, has been restored. The original yellowish-grey stone exhibits a stugged finish and polished quoins.

Plean

In Stirlingshire the *Bishopbriggs Sandstone* was worked as the '*Plean White Freestone*' at Plean or Blackcraig Quarry situated to the south-west of Plean House, Kilsyth between Bannockburn and Larbert. It was described as a pale buff-grey, medium-grained, slightly micaceous sandstone and was about 18m thick.[33]

The only large building known to have been built of Plean stone in central Edinburgh is the former Catholic Apostolic Church[34], now **Mansfield Place Church** [151], built between 1873 and 1885. In the prolonged and interrupted work, a Carboniferous sandstone from Woodburn, Northumberland was also used. It is not possible to be sure which stone is which in this building but it is likely that the Plean stone forms the bulk of the greyish-buff rock-faced walls with polished or tooled quoins. Weathering is particularly marked around the windows especially at the south-west end. The spokes of the wheel window at the west end are particularly badly scaled. Plean was also used in the **Great Michael Home & Links House** building (1878-79) (formerly the Scottish Co-operative Wholesale Society), at least for the north-eastern extension of 1885, at Links Place, Leith. The two stones seen in the **Meadows Pillars** [158] (Figure 6.2) are little weathered today though in 1893 they were said not to be standing well.[35]

Dullatur

The *Bishopbriggs Sandstone* was also worked at Dullatur Quarry, near Kilsyth. The quarry, reported to be in operation in the 1860s, yielded a medium-grained, loosely cemented, white to light brown sandstone.[36] The quarry face was stated to be 32m high but workable stone ranged between 12 and 22m thick. Examples of the stone's use in Edinburgh include:

Merchant's Hall [89] (1865-66; completed 1901), Hanover Street.

Capability Scotland Westerlea School (1860-69), Ellersly Road. Weathering badly.

Polmaise

In the Stirling district, between the *Orchard* and *Calmy* limestones (Figure 3.4), extensive quarrying took place at two quarries at Polmaise and Dunmore in sandstone known locally as the '*Cowie Rock*' which is about 52m thick.

Fresh Polmaise stone was described by Craig as cream or white in colour and of a very fine texture. Like Plean stone it was rarely used on its own in Edinburgh. Even at the end of the 19th century, the recently completed Italianate **McEwan Hall** [37] (1888-97), where Polmaise was used with Prudham stone and red Corsehill pillars (Plate 8), and the **Medical School** [36] (1876-86) were said to be showing signs of weathering.[37] Much of this weathering has been made good. Polmaise stone was used in the **Central Public Library** [24] (1887-90), George IV Bridge. The grey-yellowish stone shows some brown staining. Bedding is not clearly marked on the polished faces. Generally the stone has stood well but some stone replacement has been done recently. On the north-east side of the eastern of the two **Meadows Pillars** [158] (Figure 6.2) the Polmaise sample is worn and chipped. Other examples of the '*Cowie Rock*' from Polmaise include:

Palmerston Place Church [70] (1873-75). Arches and columns inside are of pink Peterhead granite.

Nos. 42 & 43 Drumsheugh Gardens [74] (1877).

Debenhams [94] (1882-84), 109-112 Princes Street. (formerly Liberal and Conservative Clubs).
North Morningside United Presbyterian Church (1879-81), 15 Chamberlain Road. With Dunmore stone.

Dunmore

Stone from the original Dunmore Quarry near Cowie, Stirling, was described by Craig as creamy in colour and of a hard, fine-grained texture. He noted that the stone 'in some parts shows a great number of small round holes, which are discernible when polishing'.[38] In the examples given by Craig, the stone had not weathered well. Large quantities of Dunmore stone were used in the tenements of Marchmont.[39] Stone from the original Dunmore Quarry was also used for the following buildings:
Coltbridge Hall (St George's School) (1875), Coltbridge Terrace.
North Morningside United Presbyterian Church (1879-81), 15 Chamberlain Road. With Polmaise stone.
A new quarry at Dunmore, about 1.6km east of the former working, was opened in 1985 by Scottish Natural Stones Ltd. The stone is a whitish grey to pale brown fine- to medium-grained sandstone. It has been used, for example, in the frontage of the **Trustees Savings Bank** [109] (1986), 120-124 George Street.[40] The paving in the entrance hall and atrium used pink granite from the Ross of Mull.

Giffnock

The *Giffnock Sandstone* lies between the *Lyoncross* and *Orchard* limestones[41] and was formerly exposed at quarries in Giffnock, near Glasgow. In the famous Braidbar Quarries a thickness of about 18m of stone was worked, the top 9m of which was termed 'Moor Rock', a somewhat porous and less valuable material. The quality of the underlying 'Liver Rock' was such that eventually it was mined in order to avoid removing the overlying inferior rock.[42] The principal market was Glasgow although Craig records Giffnock stone in his list of building stones used in Edinburgh.[43]

Braehead

Braehead Quarry, near Fauldhouse worked sandstone in the *Lower Coal Measures*. It produced a medium to coarse-grained sandstone, locally pebbly, of a pale yellowish brown to brownish grey colour. In the years up to closure of the quarry in 1939 the stone, although soft, was said to stand well, and was widely used for rubble work, lintels, wall copings, etc.[44] Examples in Edinburgh include:

Villas at west end of Comiston Drive.

Alma Lodge, Midmar Drive.

Villas in Grange Loan. Built in grounds of Grange House.

Villas in Mayfield Road, Esslemont Road and **Ross Road**. Facing stone with Hawkhill Wood rubble work.

Auchinlea

The Auchinlea and North Auchinlea quarries lie about 1.6km north-east of Cleland near Motherwell. This *Middle Coal Measures* sandstone is 18m thick on average although at North Auchinlea Quarry as much as 27m of sandstone was exposed at one time. It is a drab, medium-grained, stone sometimes micaceous or with ferruginous specks[45] and described by C T Clough (of the Geological Survey) as 'a yellowish freestone, not so hard as to be difficult to work'. The stone was much used in Edinburgh about the 1880s, for example in **Roseburn Terrace** (1882), but went into disuse with the introduction of the harder stone from Northumberland.[46] Other buildings where use of this sandstone may be seen include:

South Buchanan Street tenements [155] (1878-81).

Villas at Trinity (1883).

STONE FROM THE CARBONIFEROUS OF THE SCOTTISH BORDERS AND ENGLAND

As demand for sandstone for building declined, the Scottish Midland Valley quarries faced competition from the large quarries in Lower Carboniferous sandstones of northern England, in particular Prudham, Gunnerton, Doddington and Cragg, all of which supplied stone to Edinburgh in the closing years of last century. Transport was made easier as railway links with Edinburgh increased. Many other Northumberland quarries, including Darney and Blaxter, have supplied stone at intervals during the last 100 years. Blaxter continues to operate today. In the 1920s a limited amount of stone was also brought from Scottish Borders quarries by rail.

The recent demand for matching stone for restoration and repairs has encouraged the use of stone from numerous English quarries working sandstones in the Upper Carboniferous *Millstone Grit* and some in the *Coal Measures*. Currently, stone from Stainton, County Durham and Stanton Moor, Derbyshire, appear to be especially popular. Major developments around Lothian Road have employed these and other stone products.

Swinton and Whitsome Newton

Quarries at Swinton and Whitsome Newton in Berwickshire worked sandstone of the *Cementstone Group*. According to Watson (1911), Swinton stone, which was a 'delicate pink tint being highly esteemed by architects', was sent to Edinburgh in 'considerable quantities . . . for building villas'.[47] Swinton stone was used for the walls of the **Hall of Honour, National War Memorial** [9] (1924-27) at **Edinburgh Castle**.

An example of stone from Whitsome Newton, described as being of a warm cream colour and of a fine texture easily wrought, may be seen in the **Meadows Pillars** and **Sundial** [158] (Figures 6.2 and 6.3).[48]

Fairloans

North-east of Newcastleton, sandstone was once quarried at Fairloans in the *Larriston Sandstone* of the *Border Group* (partly equivalent to the *Fell Sandstone Group* of Northumberland).[49] Stone brought to Edinburgh from this locality was 'capable of a high polish' and was 'greatly used for monumental purposes'.[50]

Doddington

Sandstones of the *Fell Sandstone Group* of Northumberland have proved to be a valuable source of good building stone. Edinburgh has examples from a number of quarries, particularly Doddington[51, 52] and Glanton Pike.[53]

Few sandstones have such a characteristic appearance as the locally cross-bedded, light purplish pink sandstone from Doddington near Wooler in Northumberland which was extensively used in Edinburgh from the 1880s. It was often used for dress-ings with Hailes stone as at the **Royal Observatory** (1892), Blackford Hill, and with Hawkhill Wood stone at the **Reid Memorial Church** (1929-33), West Savile

Terrace. Doddington stone is hard and compact. It has stood well as may be observed in the cleaned north-east corner block of **North St David Street/St Andrew Square** [116] (1899; former Scottish Equitable Assurance building) (Plate 9). Some red staining brought out by cleaning is evident, particularly at the tops of the dormers. Individual stones show cross-bedding but this is generally quite faint. In North St Andrew Street some of the stones are cracked. Rock-faced Doddington stone can be seen at **No. 65 George Street** [107]. Doddington stone was used again in the early 20th century extension to the former **General Post Office** [132] (1908-09) where it can be clearly seen from the North Bridge against the grey Binny stone of the rest of the building. Other examples of Doddington stone can be seen to good advantage at:

Methodist Central Hall [54] (1899-1901), Tollcross.

National War Memorial, Edinburgh Castle [9] (1924-27).

George Watson's College (1930), Colinton Road.

Royal (Dick) Veterinary College [46] (1906-16), Summerhall. With 'pink' Hailes.

Cragg

Quarries at Cragg near Bellingham,[54] working sandstone of the *Scremerston Coal Group*, supplied much building stone to Edinburgh. Cragg sandstone can be seen at the 'new' **Old Waverley Hotel** [118] on Princes Street built in 1883-87. Here, the weathered polished stone appears grey although it has been cleaned. It cannot be examined at street level. The quoins have weathered at the north-west corner of the building and the ornament above the lintel at the west end of the building also shows signs of weathering. The building has Peterhead granite columns around the windows. A large piece of the Cragg stone has broken off the block in one of the **Meadows Pillars** [158] (Figure 6.2) but the example in the **Sundial** (Figure 6.3) remains unweathered. Craig gives **Merchiston Crescent** (1888) as a further example of Cragg stone.[55]

Probably the finest example of the use of Cragg in Edinburgh is **Jenner's Store** [105] (1893-95), Princes Street. Most of the detail is above street level where extensive replacement of weathered stone was undertaken in 1995, using Blaxter stone, a very good match for Cragg.

Blaxter

Stone from Blaxter Quarry, Elsdon, Otterburn, was extensively used in Edinburgh after the First World War and the Head Office of Blaxter's Ltd. was located in the city during the 1950s. The quarry is currently operated by Tynecastle Stone (under Haydens Northern of Gateshead). The stone is a fine- to medium-grained, buff, slightly micaceous sandstone of the *Lower Limestone Group*. In the facing of the **National Library of Scotland** [22] (1937-1955) on George IV Bridge the fine-grained stone is of uniform colour and the bedding is not obvious. The lower part of the facing is rusticated on a grey Creetown granite base. In the forty years since completion there has been little deterioration apart from some slight pitting of the stone near the lower windows. The **Royal Museum of Scotland Lecture Theatre** [27] (1958-61) in Lothian Street has a uniform polished facing of a lighter colour and slightly coarser grain. Brown specks and concretions can be seen in this stone which again exhibits little in the way of obvious bedding. An early use of Blaxter stone (along with Denwick stone) in the form of good quality ashlar was in the construction of the houses in **Arden Street** [51] and adjoining streets in Marchmont between 1905-11.[56] There are many other good examples of Blaxter stone:

Sun Alliance Insurance Building [100] (1955), 68 George Street.
Lothian House [58] (1936), Lothian Road.
Grant Institute of Geology, Kings Buildings (1930-31), West Mains Road.
Scottish & Newcastle Breweries, Head Office [145] (1961), Holyrood Road.
Fountainbridge Telephone Exchange [56] (1949-52), Gardner's Crescent.
Standard Life Assurance Office Extension [111] (1972), Thistle Street.
Burtons [166] (1906-07), 30-31 Princes Street. (formerly R W Forsyth Ltd.)

Darney

Sandstone of the *Lower Limestone Group* from Darney, West Woodburn is finer grained and paler than Blaxter stone. Quarrying at Darney stopped in 1984 but is listed under Natural Stone Products in the BGS Directory of Mines and Quarries (1998).[57] It was used in the **High Court of Justiciary** [14] (1934-37), Bank Street. This uniform buff-coloured stone is polished and rusticated to the balcony level and shows no signs of weathering. At the **Royal Bank of Scotland** [122] (1936) (formerly National Bank of Scotland), No. 42 St Andrew Square, recently cleaned Darney stone is set off against a Rubislaw (Aberdeen) grey granite base. The polished stone is rusticated up to the first floor level. Close examination shows that the buff-yellowish stone is full of tiny brown specks. Stone from Darney and Leoch Quarry, Dundee was used in the construction of the **Usher Hall** [64] (1910-14). Darney stone, specially polished to resist the adherence of soot, was used in the building of **St Andrew's House** [135] (1936-39) described as 'by far the most impressive work of architecture in Scotland before the wars'. The base course is of Creetown grey granite. Another use in the 1930s includes the **City Chambers extension** [15] (1930-34) in Cockburn Street. A more recent example includes **No. 45 George Street** [108] (1974).

Prudham

From the end of the 19th century, building stones were brought by rail from the north-east of England. *Middle Limestone Group* sandstone from Prudham, near Hexham in central Northumberland, was much used from the mid-1880s until 1970. It is a cream-coloured, slightly micaceous coarse-grained sandstone containing tiny brown specks. Fresh stone seen in the cladding above the entrance to the **St Andrew Square Bus Station** [121] (1970), shows brown patches and lamination. Prudham stone was used at the turn of the century for the **Balmoral Hotel** [2] (1902), East End, Princes Street, where its polished surface was very badly weathered, particularly the north and west elevations. Restoration of the stonework, was carried out between 1989 and 1991 using Dunhouse stone.[58] Of all the stones used in the **Meadows Pillars** [158] (Figure 6.2) the Prudham blocks on the east pillar are the worst affected, almost the whole worked surface having weathered away. Large quantities of Prudham stone were used in the **Marchmont** tenements between 1876 and 1914.[59]

Other examples include:

Villas in Craighall Gardens (1885-89)

Crown Office [26] (1886-88), (formerly Heriot Watt College), Chambers Street.

London Street Primary School [150] (1887), East London Street.

McEwan Hall [37] (1888-97), Teviot Place.

Norwich Union Life Insurance Group [179] (1970), 32 St Andrew Square.

Gunnerton

This medium hard, fine grained, creamy white sandstone from the *Middle Limestone Group* was quarried at Barrasford, near Hexham.[60] It was used in 1885 in the building of tenements in Morningside. It was also used in George Craig's reconstruction of the former **Yardheads School** (1887), Giles Street, Leith. By 1892, the stone was already showing signs of weathering at the **Meadows Pillars** [158] (Figure 6.2).[61]

Dunhouse

The quarry is situated near Staindrop, west of Darlington, County Durham. It has worked since the early 1900s and has been in the hands of the present owners, Dunhouse Quarry Company, since 1933.[62] The sandstone which is in the Upper Carboniferous *Millstone Grit*, is a fine-grained, buff coloured stone.

In Edinburgh, it has been used widely in repairs and restoration work, for example, in General Accident's offices at **Nos. 1–8 Atholl Crescent** (1982-84) and **Canning Street** (1985) [66]. At the peak of this work, the project was using 60% of the quarry's output.[63] The staircases were rebuilt in Woodkirk Brown York stone. The **Holiday Inn Crowne Plaza Hotel** [183] (formerly Scandic Crown Hotel) (1989-90), High Street, used rubble and dressed Dunhouse stone including a colonnade of thirteen arches. Between 1989 and 1991, 2300 cubic feet (65m^3) of Dunhouse stone was used for restoration and repairs to the **Balmoral Hotel** [2] mainly on the east and west elevations and in restoring the cornice of the clock tower.[64]

Other buildings employing Dunhouse stone include:

Marks & Spencers Store [95] (1980), 104 Princes Street.

Exchange Plaza [161] (1997), Lothian Road.

Stainton

For the past few years much of the repair work on Edinburgh's older buildings has been carried out with buff coloured Stainton stone (*Millstone Grit*) from Barnard Castle, County Durham. This stone often exhibits a brown streaked and speckled appearance, exemplified by the cladding of the extension to **John Lewis' building** [177] on Leith Walk. The more uniform buff colouring is a good match for several of the local Lower Carboniferous stones. It has been used for example for indent repairs (1985) at the **Bank of Scotland** [13], the Mound where it matches Binny, and at the **Royal Museum of Scotland** [27], Chambers Street where it substitutes for Hermand. It is also utilised as a facing stone on recent buildings in central Edinburgh as at **Nos. 40-42 George Street** [102]. Here the sandstone is broached above street level to match the surrounding buildings which are probably built of Craigleith sandstone. Below street level the stone is rock faced. Stainton has been considerably used for restoration work in the mistaken view that it was a good colour match for Craigleith.[65] Ironically, Stainton stone has been used for the facade to the entrance to **Sainsbury's plc Supermarket** (1993), Queensferry Road, site of the former Craigleith Quarry (Chapter 7). A brief history of this famous quarry was published in an excellent leaflet sponsored by Sainsburys plc.[66]

At Castle Terrace, the major **Saltire Court** [63] development (1991; Plate 10) including the **New Traverse Theatre** utilised Stainton stone facing together with red sandstone quoins from the specially re-opened Newton Quarry, Gatelawbridge.[67] The base course is composed of a dark grey, coarse-grained diorite (?) from Scandinavia (Edalhammer and Blaubrun). Small bivalve fossils, coloured deep orange-brown, can be seen in some of the blocks of Stainton stone. Other recent examples of Stainton stone can be seen at:

Albany Street/Broughton Street Office Development [148] (1984).
Royal Hospital for Sick Children [49] (1997), Sciennes Road.
Standard Life building [162] (1997), Lothian Road.
97 George Street [175] (1980). Restoration; and used for central portico and indents.

Catcastle

Yellowish grey to buff, medium to coarse-grained sandstone (*Millstone Grit*) from Catcastle Quarry, Lartington, Barnard Castle is worked by the Dunhouse Quarry Company Ltd. Stone has been used recently at **No.10 George Street** [173] (1990) and the **Sheriff Court House** [23] (1997), 27-29 Chambers Street.

Wellfield

'Crossland Hill Hard York Stone' is quarried in the *Rough Rock* (*Millstone Grit*) at Wellfield (Crossland Hill) Quarry, west of Huddersfield, by Johnsons Wellfield Ltd.

This sandstone has recently been used to face the front of the **Sheraton Hotel** [61] (1985) in Lothian Road. It may be compared there with the *Middle Coal Measures* stone from Woodkirk used as cladding on the adjacent **Capital House** [60]. The Sheraton exhibits a polished fawn sandstone of a slightly lighter shade than the greenish grey Woodkirk stone which is less uniformly coloured. The Wellfield stone is also somewhat micaceous and the bedding is a little clearer. Some stones are set on end. To match with the adjacent Film House, the rustication on Capital House is taken to the same level. Other examples of recently used Wellfield stone include:

British Home Stores [99] (1965), Princes Street.

George Square Lecture Theatre [44] (1967).

United Distillers House (1981), 33 Ellersly Road.

Scottish Life Assurance Company [112] (1962), North St David Street.

Stoke Hall

Stoke Hall Quarry, near Eyam in Derbyshire (Stoke Hall Quarry Ltd.), supplies a fine-grained orange-buff sandstone, extracted from the *Millstone Grit*. This stone was used for the first time in Edinburgh to face the **Edinburgh Conference Centre** [164] (1996) in Morrison Street. In this building the large curved modules are pre-cast concrete, coloured to match the fresh sandstone.

Stanton Moor

Stone has been quarried historically over an extensive area of Stanton Moor, near Matlock, Derbyshire in the *Ashover Grit* (*Millstone Grit*). This account refers mainly to 'Stanton Moor' sandstone from Palmer's/Dale View Quarry, Stanton-in-Peak, Stanton Moor. This quarry which is currently operated by the Stancliffe Stone Company Ltd. was reopened in 1983. Other quarries in the district include Birchover (Natural Stone Products, Ennstone plc) and New Pillough, Stanton-in-Peak and Wattscliffe, Elton (Block Stone Ltd., Realstone plc).[68]

The 'Stanton Moor' sandstone of Palmer's Quarry is a medium- to fine-grained buff sandstone, variably tinted pink, orange and grey, sometimes in the same block. This variety of texture and colour, combined with ready availability and good weathering resistance, has made the stone a ubiquitous choice where matching stone can no longer be obtained, particularly for those from the Carboniferous of the

Midland Valley. Stone from Stanton Moor may be seen in many parts of Edinburgh (Appendix 3). Examples of restoration work include **No. 32 St Mary's Street** [181] (1983) and **No. 35 Heriot Row** [88] (1998). Currently, the stone is being used for major developments including **The Dynamic Earth** building, Holyrood Road.

Stancliffe

The *Millstone Grit* sandstone of Stancliffe Quarry, Darley Dale, recently closed, has also been used for repair work, especially in the New Town (Appendix 3). **Nos. 15-21 Palmerston Place** [68], originally constructed in the 1880s using *Binny Sandstone* from Dalmeny (see above), were repaired with stone from Stancliffe Darley Dale and Dunhouse. Stone from Stancliffe was also used in tenement restorations in **Drummond Street** (1985).

Springwell

A *Middle Coal Measures* sandstone from Springwell, Gateshead, Tyne and Wear has been used as cladding for **Apex House** [152] (1975) on the north east corner of the junction of Leith Walk and Annandale Street. Polished throughout, this medium-grained, yellowish stone appears rather uniform and featureless. The stone was also used for the restoration of the front elevation of **Nos. 8-11 Royal Crescent** [167] (1979).

Woodkirk

The fine-grained, greenish-grey sandstone quarried at Woodkirk, Morley, Yorkshire has been used as cladding on **Capital House** [60], Lothian Road (see Wellfield, above) and re-cladding at **C & A Stores** [119], 33-38 Princes Street. The latter was originally clad with stone from Blaxter in 1957. Woodkirk stone was also used for the **Hilton National Hotel** [79] (1978), Belford Road.

Heworthburn

Middle Coal Measures sandstone has been quarried at Heworthburn near Felling in Tyne and Wear. This fine-grained, light yellow-brown speckled stone can be observed at **No.2 George Street** [104] near the east end on the south side. The cladding which has some darker patches is not seen at street level because the lower part of the building is faced with black gabbro. The west end of the building above the first floor level is much redder than the front on George Street. Other notable examples in Princes Street are **Frasers Department Store** [165](1935), **Nos. 145-149 Princes Street** and **Nos. 91-93 Princes Street** [97] (1960s).

STONE FROM THE PERMIAN AND TRIASSIC ('NEW RED SANDSTONE') OF DUMFRIES & GALLOWAY AND CUMBRIA

The Permian red sandstone from the Dumfries area, quarried at Locharbriggs, Corncockle, Gatelawbridge and Closeburn and the Triassic red sandstone of Corsehill, became available in Edinburgh from about 1850 onwards after the eventual completion of the Caledonian Railway line.

Locharbriggs

At Locharbriggs Quarry, Dumfries, dune bedded red sandstones of the *Locharbriggs Sandstone Formation* have been worked for 150 years by Baird & Stevenson (Quarrymasters) Ltd. The rock is medium- to fine-grained red sandstone, very well sorted, and consists of sub- to well-rounded quartz grains, coated with iron oxide and weakly cemented by silica. Some feldspar is also present.

One of the most prominent buildings in the city centre built of stone from Locharbriggs is the brick-red **Caledonian Hotel** [65] (1899-1903) (Plate 11) which has been described as 'a wonderfully blousy red sandstone intrusion into classical Edinburgh'.[69] Some stone from Corncockle Quarry was also used. The recently cleaned, fine- to medium-grained sandstone shows good dune bedding in its polished surfaces. Eight impressive Corinthian monoliths surround the entrance to the adjacent former station of the Caledonian Railway which brought the stone to Edinburgh. There is weathering on the easternmost column and on the east side of the building high up between the two-storied dormer windows but generally the Locharbriggs stone has stood well. At ground level some plastic repair has been carried out where some of the sharp arrises were becoming eroded by constant evaporation of splash-back water from the pavement. Most of this repair work, however, was undertaken to replace mechanical damage caused by rusting railings, now replaced. Stone from Locharbriggs was also used for the **Lauriston Place Fire Station** [160] (1897-1901) and slightly later, together with sandstone from Closeburn, in the **Edinburgh College of Art** [30] (1906-10). Some 60 years later, stone from Locharbriggs Quarry was still available for the building of the **Art College extension** in 1972. The older buildings in the area are showing some signs of weathering with bedding picked out in the western side of the Fire Station by differential erosion.

Corncockle

Corncockle Quarry, north of Lochmaben, also has a long history of working until the mid 1950s. It was re-opened in 1986 and Onyx Contractors work it on an intermittent basis, supplying stone for specific projects. The Permian *Corncockle Sandstone Formation* consists of thick beds of aeolian, fine to medium-grained, well-sorted, red sandstone, composed of quartz with minor amounts of feldspar.

Corncockle stone was much used in Edinburgh between c.1880 to c.1900, particularly for dressings on Edinburgh Board schools.[70] An example is the **Scotch Whisky Heritage Centre** (formerly Castlehill School) [10] (1888) at the top of the Royal Mile, where greyish, coarse, squared-rubble Hailes is contrasted with deep red, diagonally droved, Corncockle dressings. The detail is still sharp at lower levels but there is scaling in the dressings and detail in the upper part of the building, especially on the north side. At the base of the **Meadows Sundial** [158] (Figure 6.3) the Corncockle sample shows no appreciable weathering. Other examples include:

Leith Academy Lochend Annex (1885-87), Lochend Road.

Royal Bank of Scotland [39] (1902), Nicolson Street

Milton House School [144] (1886), Canongate. With 'grey' Hailes.

Gatelawbridge

Permian aeolian dune-bedded sandstones of the *Thornhill Sandstone Formation* have been worked at Gatelawbridge[71, 72] and Closeburn quarries near Thornhill.[73]

Gatelawbridge has been worked from the 17th century onwards and was at one time leased to Robert Paterson (1717-1801), alias 'Old Mortality' (of Sir Walter Scott's novel). Although much used in Glasgow, Gatelawbridge stone is only known to have contributed to one building in Edinburgh situated on the north side of Rose Street [187], immediately behind Jenner's store. This was designed as workshops for

Charles Jenner, the first part built in 1890 and the second, including the **Abbotsford Bar** [187] in 1902.[74] This bright red sandstone from near Thornhill clearly shows dune cross-bedding at ground level on the polished west and south sides of the building. On the west and north sides the building is rock-faced, with polished quoins. Above street level on the west end, the stone is lightly stugged with smoothed margins. There is some efflorescence above the windows at the east end, perhaps a consequence of cleaning which has brought salts out of the stone. Gatelawbridge stone is scaling on both of the **Meadows Pillars** [158] (Figure 6.2).

Newton Quarry at Gatelawbridge was re-opened in 1986 by Scottish Natural Stones Ltd. It has supplied stone for **Saltire Court** [63], Castle Terrace (Plate 10) (see also Stainton) and the **Edinburgh Solicitors Property Centre** [174] 85 George Street.

Closeburn

A good example of the use of the deep red sandstone (*Thornhill Sandstone Formation*) from the former Closeburn Quarry, south of Thornhill, is the **King's Theatre** [157], Tollcross, built in 1904 and repaired with indents of Corsehill in the 1980s. The stone was also used for the tower of **Candlish Church** (1915), Merchiston, along with rubble work from Hailes.

Corsehill

Triassic red sandstone (*St Bees Sandstone*) was worked at Corsehill Quarry, Annan from the 1880s until the mid 1950s. The quarry was reopened in 1981 and is currently operated by Onyx Contractors. In contrast to the other red sandstones from Dumfries & Galloway, those of Corsehill are of water-lain origin. Beds are generally thinner, but are laterally continuous. Internal cross-bedding within some beds is discernible but is much smaller scale and less prominent than in the desert sandstones. Being fine-grained and capable of carrying a sharp arris, the stone has traditionally been used for all kinds of inside and ornamental work and carving, and is noted for its use, not only as a construction stone, but also for monuments, panels, quoins and plinths.

Corsehill stone is a warm red, fine-grained, slightly micaceous sandstone. It has been used at **No. 70 Princes Street** [98] (1886) although not at street level. At the

National Portrait Gallery [114] (1885-90) in Queen Street, where stone from the Dumfries area was first used on a large scale in Edinburgh,[75] it is not possible to distinguish Corsehill sandstone from the Cumbrian equivalent, formerly worked at Moat, near Carlisle, which was used with it (Plate 9). Here, damage to the stone was so severe that it was necessary to remove the parapet and pinnacles of this 'Doge's Palace' in 1980.[76] However, it is likely that it is the Moat stone that weathered poorly as Corsehill stone from the re-opened quarry has excellent resistance to weathering. Restoration of the detail will proceed using matching Dumfries stone removed from an old former Caledonian Railway bridge in Leith and from the present Corsehill quarry. The disabled access in Queen Street appears to be of sandstone from Locharbriggs. Examples of both Corsehill and Moat stone at the **Meadows Pillars** [158] (Figure 6.2) are weathered and much of the original detail has disappeared. However, the Corsehill sample in the nearby **Meadows Sundial** (Figure 6.3) is weathering well. Other red sandstones from the Dumfries area show slightly better weathering properties. The use of Corsehill dressings with 'pink' and 'grey' Hailes is well displayed in **Roseburn Primary School** (1893), Roseburn Street (Plate 5). Further uses of Corsehill can be seen at **St James Episcopal Church** (1885), Inverleith Row, the **Royal Hospital for Sick Children** [49] (1892), Sciennes Road, and **No. 1 Cluny Gardens** (with 'pink' Hailes).

Lazonby

Dune-bedded, pink to red-brown medium-grained sandstone of the *Penrith Sandstone Formation* of Permian age is quarried near Lazonby, north of Penrith.[77] Currently marketed as 'Stoneraise Red' by Realstone Ltd. and as 'Plumpton Red Lazonby' by Cumbria Stone Quarries Ltd., the stone has been used in Edinburgh, for example in the interior access to the new crypt or undercroft of the **High Kirk of St Giles** [18] (1984).

Moat

Bright red, water-lain sandstones of the *St Bees Sandstone Formation* (*Sherwood Sandstone Group*) of early Triassic age were worked intermittently at Moat Quarry, north of Longtown. This quarry formerly supplied stone for the **National Portrait Gallery** [114] (1885-90) (see also Corsehill) and for **Couper Street School** (1889-90).[78]

Stone from the Permian and Triassic ('New Red Sandstone') of Moray

Permian and Triassic sandstones of the 'New Red Sandstone' in Moray are typically highly siliceous and well cemented. Colours vary considerably but typically yellow, buff and fawn sandstones predominate unlike the bright red stones of southern Scotland and Cumbria.

Clashach

On the Moray coast, the *Sandstones of Hopeman* have long been used as a source of good building stone.[79] Clashach Quarry has been operated by Moray Stone Cutters, recently supplying stone to the Stirling Stone Group for some major building projects in Edinburgh. Sandstones from Clashach are typically yellow to buff coloured, but can be variegated with brown limonite wisps and patches. Recently, dull red stone has also been extracted. The sandstone is siliceous and composed of well rounded quartz grains with feldspar.[80] Large scale cross-bedding is taken as an indication of dune formation although locally, water-lain pebbly sandstones are also present. These rocks have yielded reptilian footprints but little else in the way of fossils.

Recent major building projects using Clashach stone cladding include the **Museum of Scotland**[81] (extension to the Royal Museum of Scotland) [27](1998), Chambers Street (Plate 12) and the **Scottish Widows Fund and Life Assurance Society** building [163] (1997), Morrison Street (Plate 13). The latter has also used Clashach stone, on account of its strength, for external paving. The **Paton Building**, Nos. 1–3 York Place [176], originally constructed in sandstone from Craigleith, has been splendidly re-faced in Clashach stone (Plate 14).[82] Buildings where Clashach stone has been used in recent years include:

Nos. 202-254 Canongate [143] (1958-66).

Nos. 23 - 24 Fettes Row [87] (1974). Repairs.

Chessels Court [185] (1969), Canongate.

Moray House Teacher Training College [184] (1970), Holyrood Road. Repairs.

Edinburgh Castle [9] (1978) restoration work.

Spynie

Upper Triassic sandstones, worked at Spynie Quarry near Elgin, have been used in several Edinburgh buildings in recent years.[83] An aeolian origin is ascribed to the sandstone which is cross-bedded, yellowish grey, very fine-grained, hard and locally highly siliceous.[84] Examples of the use of this stone include:

83-89 Great King Street [169] (1982). Mouldings.
39 Howe Street [168] (1982). Mouldings.
1a St Bernards Crescent [170] (1981). Indents.
12 Leslie Place [171] (1981). Indents.

REFERENCES

1. Gowans, Sir J., Building stones of Scotland. *The Builder*, 41, 1881, p.673.

2. Mackie, A., Sandstone quarrying in Angus - Some thoughts on an old craft, *The Edinburgh Geologist*, 8, 1980, p.14-25.

3. Watson, J.W., *British and foreign building stones*, Cambridge University Press, 1911, p.113.

4. Harry, W.T., The geology of the Dundee district from its quarries, *Quarry Managers' Journal*, 1952, p.91.

5. Bremner, D., *The industries of Scotland, Edinburgh*, Adam and Charles Black 1869, p.422.

6. McMillan, A.A. *Quarries of Scotland*. Technical Advice Note No.12. Edinburgh: Historic Scotland, 1997.

7. MacGregor, A.G., The mineral resources of the Lothians, *Geological Survey Wartime Pamphlet*, No.45, 1945, p.18.

8. Craig, G., Building stones used in Edinburgh: their geological sources, relative durability and other characteristics, *Transactions of the Edinburgh Geological Society*, 1893, 6, p.259-260, 263-264.

9. Forsyth, Charles, On the mines, minerals and geology of West Lothian, *Transactions of the Highland and Agricultural Society of Scotland*, (New Series) 10, 1846, p.229-273.

10. Bremner, G., *op. cit.*, p.413.

11. Gowans, Sir J., *op.cit.*, p.673.

12. MacGregor, A.G., *op. cit.*, p.18.

13. Tait, D., The occurrence of petroliferous sandstones in the Carboniferous rocks of Scotland and their relation to certain black sandstones, *Transactions of the Edinburgh Geological Society*, 12, 1932, p.94.

14. *The Builder*, August 11, 1845.

15. Gowans, J., *Model dwelling houses*, T. and A. Constable, 1886, p.55-57.

16. Craig, G., *op. cit.* p.262.

17. *ibid.*

18. Smith, G., Account of the quarries of sandstone in the Edinburgh and Glasgow districts, and of the principal slate quarries in Scotland, *Prize Essays and Transactions of the Highland and Agricultural Society of Scotland*, (New Series) 4, 1835, p.87.

19. Bremner, G., *op. cit.*, p.413.

20. Smith, G., *op. cit.*, p.87.

21. Bremner, G., *op. cit.*, p.413.

22. Craig, G., *op. cit.*, p.264.

23. Watson, J.W., *op cit.*, p.125, 275.

24. Francis, E.H., The economic geology of the Fife Coalfields, Area II, Cowdenbeath and Central Fife, 2nd Edition, *Memoirs of the Geological Survey (Scotland)*, 1961, p.14-15.

25. Gowans, Sir J., *op. cit.*, p.673.

26. Carruthers, R.G., The geology of the oil-shale fields in The oil-shales of the Lothians, 3rd Edition, *Memoirs of the Geological Survey (Scotland)*, 1927, p.97

27. Gowans, Sir J., *op. cit.*, p.673.

28. Craig, G., *op. cit.*, p.267.

29. *ibid.*

30. Clough, C.T., Hinxman, L.W., Grant Wilson, J.S., Crampton, C.B., Wright, W.B., Bailey, E.B., Anderson, E.M. and Carruthers, R.G., The geology of the Glasgow district, *Memoirs of the Geological Survey (Scotland)*, 1911, p.237.

31. Forsyth, I.H., The Stratigraphy of the Upper Limestone Group (E1 and E2 Stages of the Namurian) in the Glasgow district, *Report of the Institute of Geological Sciences*, 82/4, 1982, 21pp.

32. *ibid.*

33. Dinham, C.H. and Haldane, D., The economic geology of the Stirling and Clackmannan Coalfield, *Memoirs of the Geological Survey (Scotland)*, 1920, p.196-197.

34. Craig, G., *op. cit*, p.262.

35. *ibid*, p.262, 268.

36. Robertson, T. and Haldane, D., The economic geology of the Central Coalfield, Area 1 Kilsyth and Kirkintilloch, *Memoirs of the Geological Survey of Great Britain (Scotland)*, 1937, p.132.

37. Craig, G. *op. cit.*, 1893, p.261.

38. *ibid.*, p.265.

39. Cant, M., *Marchmont in Edinburgh*, J. Donald, Ltd., Edinburgh, 1984, p.143.

40. Anon. Scottish Revival, *Stone Industries*, 9, November 1985, p.20-21.

41. Forsyth, I.H., *op. cit.*, 1982, p.8.

42. Hinxman, L.W., Anderson, E.M. and Carruthers, R.G., Economic geology of the Central Coalfield of Scotland, Area IV Paisley, Barrhead and Renfrew, *Memoirs of the Geological Survey (Scotland)*, 1920, p.97–98.

43. Craig, G., *op. cit.*, p.266.

44. MacGregor, A.G., *op. cit.*, p.20.

45. Watson, J., *op. cit.*, p. 136.

46. Clough, C.T., The economic geology of the Central Coalfield of Scotland, Area VII, Rutherglen, Hamilton and Wishaw, *Memoirs of the Geological Survey (Scotland)*, 1920, p. 124.

47. Watson, J., *op. cit.*, p.112.

48. Gowans, Sir J., The Memorial Masons' Pillars in *Model Dwelling Houses*, T. and A. Constable, 1886, p.55-57.

49. Lumsden, G.I., Tulloch, W., Howells, M.F. and Davies, A., The geology of the neighbourhood of Langholm, *Memoir of the Geological Survey of Great Britain*, Sheet 11 (Scotland), 1967, p.103.

50. Gowans, Sir J., *op. cit.*, 1881, p.673.

51. Craig, G., *op. cit.*, p.270-71.

52. Carruthers, R.G., Dinham, C.H., Burnett, G.A. and Maden, J., The geology of Belford, Holy Island and the Farne Islands, *Memoir of the Geological Survey of Great Britain*, Sheet 4 (England and Wales), 1927, p.161-162.

53. Carruthers, R.G., Burnett, G.A. and Anderson, W., The geology of the Alnwick district, *Memoir of the Geological Survey of Great Britain*, Sheet 6 (England and Wales), 1930, p.109.

54. Craig, G., *op. cit.*, p.264-265.

55. *ibid.*, p.265.

56. Cant, M., *op. cit.*, p.62.

57. Cameron, D.G., Highley, D.E., Hillier, J.A., Johnson, T.P., Linley, K.A., Mills, A.J., Smith, C.G. and White R.G. (compilers), *Directory of mines and quarries: Digital data: 01/04/98*, Keyworth, Nottingham: British Geological Survey, 1998.

58. *The Scotsman*, 8 March 1991, Ronald Banel, p.13.

59. Cant, M., *op. cit.*, p.143.

60. Craig, *op. cit.*, 1893, p.262-263.

61. *ibid.*, p.263.

62. Leary, E., *op. cit.*, p. 28.

63. *Stone Industries*, 1985 and *The Scotsman*, 17 December 1985, p.6.

64. *The Scotsman, op. cit.*, 8 March, 1991.

65. Leary, E., *op. cit*, p. 68.

66. Leaflet on *Craigleith Quarry*. London: Sainsburys plc, 1993.

67. Butcher, N.E., The Hole in the Ground, *The Edinburgh Geologist*, 26, 1991, p.12-17.

68. Leary, E., *op. cit*, p. 11, 71, 75.

69. McKean, C., *Edinburgh, An illustrated architectural guide*, 2nd Edition, Edinburgh: Royal Incorporation of Architects in Scotland, 1992, p.85.

70. Craig, G., *op. cit.*, 1893, p.268–269.

71. Craig, G., *op. cit.*, p.269–70.

72. Boyle, Robert, The economic and petrographic geology of the New Red Sandstones of the south and west of Scotland. *Transactions of the Geological Society of Glasgow*, 13, 1909, p.351–354.

73. *ibid.*

74. Gifford, J., McWilliam, C., Walker, D., *The buildings of Scotland, Edinburgh*. London: Penguin Books, 1984, p.322.

75. *The Builder*, 1885, p.350.

76. McKean, C., *op. cit.*, 1982, p.64.

77. Leary, E., *op. cit.*, p.47.

78. Craig, G., *op. cit.*, p.270.

79. Leary, E., *op. cit.*, p.20, 35.

80. Peacock, J.D., Berridge, N.G., Harris, A.L. and May, F., The geology of the Elgin district, *Memoirs of the Geological Survey of Great Britain*, Sheet 95 (Scotland), 1968, p.58-63.

81. New Civil Engineer, 24/31 July 1997, p.20-22.

82. Natural Stone Specialist, December 1998, p.11.

83. Leary, E., *op. cit.*, p.67.

84. Peacock, J.D., Berridge, N.G., Harris, A.L, and May, F., *op. cit.*, p.68-70.

APPENDIX 1 Glossary

Agglomerate: rock produced by explosive volcanic activity - coarse angular blocks in a fine-grained matrix.

Andesite: fine-grained, volcanic rock consisting of feldspar and iron-magnesian silicate minerals.

Anhydrite: mineral composed of calcium sulphate (see also gypsum).

Anticline: strata folded in the form of an arch.

Architrave: the lowest horizontal member lying above a column in a colonnaded building.

Ashlar: hewn blocks of masonry finely dressed to size and laid in courses.

Baillie: magistrate in Scottish local government

Barrack: accommodation for itinerant workers, sometimes temporary.

Basalt: black, fine-grained, basic igneous rock, commonly forming lava flows and consisting of iron oxide and silicate minerals including feldspar and pyroxene.

Bedding: natural layers formed during deposition of sediments.

Blaes: old mining term for mudstone or shale, not containing much bituminous material.

Boaster: broad-faced chisel used for dressing stones.

Braided: interwoven stream or river channels, constantly shifting through islands composed of sands, silts and clays.

Broached: Scottish term for work on stone face with pointed tool to produce vertical or horizontal furrows.

Calcite: calcium carbonate, a common constituent of limestone.

Camstone: fine-grained, calcareous stone used for whitening doorsteps.

Cementstone: fine-grained, muddy limestone.

Cladding: thin slabs of stone used as external, non-load-bearing covering to building structure.

Column: free-standing vertical member, normally circular in plan, often conforming to the classical orders.

Conglomerate: sedimentary rock consisting of water-worn pebbles bound together in a sandy matrix.

Corbel: stone or series of stones projecting from a wall used for support.

Cornstone: concretionary limestone formed under arid conditions.

Corinthian: the most ornate of the variations on post and lintel structure found in classical architecture.

Course: continuous layer of stones of uniform height.

Coursed rubble: roughly squared stones in courses to correspond with quoin and jamb stones.

Cross-bedding: in sands a series of inclined bedding planes having a relationship to the direction of current flow (also current-bedding).

Cyclothem: repeated unit in cyclic sedimentation.

Desiccation: the process of drying up.

Dimensioned stone: ashlar or stone prepared to specified dimensions.

Dip: inclination of strata to the horizontal.

Dolerite: black, medium-grained basic igneous rock consisting of iron oxide and silicate minerals including feldspar and pyroxene.

Draft: smooth strip worked on stone face to width of draft chisel.

Dressed: applied to stone with any kind of worked finish.

Droved: tooled with a broad chisel.

Dune-bedding: large-scale cross-bedding typical of sands deposited in desert and beach dunes.

Dyke: sheet-like body of igneous rock which cuts across the bedding of the sedimentary rocks (see also sill).

Efflorescence: development of crystallisation of salts on wall surfaces.

Evaporite: deposit of precipitated salt (e.g. anhydrite, gypsum), evaporation having caused the necessary concentration.

Fault: fracture in rock along which there has been an observable amount of displacement.

Feaks (Fakes): old mining term for thinly bedded shaly, micaceous sandstone or sandy shale (see also flagstone).

Feldspar: important group of rock-forming silicate minerals including silicates of sodium, potassium and calcium.

Felsite: fine-grained igneous rock consisting of feldspar and quartz.

Flagstone: fissile, micaceous laminated sandstone, suitable for roofs and pavements.

Freestone: see Liver Rock.

Gabbro: coarse-grained igneous rock consisting of feldspar and magnesium- and iron-rich silicate minerals including pyroxene and sometimes olivine.

Gin: machine used in hoisting often driven by horses.

Graben: block of the earth's crust down-thrown between two faults.

Granite: coarse-grained igneous rock consisting of quartz, feldspar and very commonly mica.

Greywacke: fine- to coarse-grained, hard sandstone consisting of mainly angular quartz and rock fragments (also known as wacke).

Gypsum: soft white mineral composed of hydrated calcium sulphate.

Indenting: Scottish term for cutting out worn or damaged stone and inserting new (indents).

Ionic: simpler variation of the post and lintel structure found in classical architecture (see also Corinthian).

Jamb: stones forming the vertical surfaces at the sides of doors or windows.

Joint: fracture in the rock with no displacement. Joints often occur in two sets, more or less vertical and at right angles to each other.

Jumper: hand tool for sinking holes in stone.

Limonite: hydrated iron oxide and hydroxide.

Lithology: character of rock in terms of composition, structure and grain size.

Liver rock: massive sandstone without discernible bedding which can be worked in all directions (also freestone).

Mash: Scottish term for Mason's steel hammer weighing 1-2kg.

Metamorphic rock: recrystallized rock derived from pre-existing rocks by action of high temperature and/or pressure in the earth's crust.

Mica: flaky complex hydrated silicate mineral.

Newel: upright column around which the steps of a spiral staircase wind.

Ostracod: minute creature which has jointed limbs and lives inside a bivalve shell.

Pilaster: shallow pier or part column projecting from a wall.

Pillar: free-standing vertical block of stone: circular or polygonal in plan.

Pillar and Stall: method of mining which involved leaving pillars of the material being mined to support the roof (also known as stoop and room).

Pitched: surfaces resembling natural rock produced by pitching tool.

Plat: platform, doorstep or landing.

Plug and Feathers: steel wedge (plug) with half-round steel strip (feathers) on either side, used for splitting stone.

Polished: stone surface worked to a very smooth finish by rubbing.

Pyroxene: group of iron and magnesium (ferro-magnesian) silicate minerals.

Quartz: common rock-forming, hard glassy mineral, silica.

Quoin: stone at external angle of wall.

Random rubble: walling of irregular unsquared stones.

Redd: quarry rubbish.

Rubble (ruble): rough uncut stones of irregular shape and size.

Rusticated joints: where margins of stones are sunk below the general face.

Sandstone: sedimentary rock composed of sand grains naturally cemented.

Scaling: stone flaking-off in thin layers.

Scleroscope: small diamond-tipped rebound hammer used for measuring hardness of a material.

Seatearth: rock composed of clay-, silt- or sand-grade material full of fossilised plant roots, representing a former soil.

Sett: stone roughly squared for paving (also calsay stones).

Sill: sheet of igneous rock intruded along the bedding planes of earlier rocks.

Sneck: small stone in squared rubble work to make up bed bonding.

Squared rubble: walling of irregular squared stones laid in courses.

Stratigraphy: study of stratified rocks including their sequence in time and the correlation of sedimentary sequences in different localities.

Stugged: pecked stone faced with a pick or pointed tool.

Syenite: coarse-grained igneous rock consisting mainly of potassium-rich feldspar and hornblende.

Till: stiff to hard clay with stones, deposited by ice (also boulder clay).

Tirr: material removed as overburden.

Tooled: dressed.

Tuff: consolidated volcanic ash.

APPENDIX 2 Sandstone quarries: locations and stratigraphy

Quarry	Location	NGR	Stratigraphy	Status, operators/owners
Auchinlea	Motherwell, Lanarkshire	NS809 591	Middle Coal Measures	
Baberton	Edinburgh	NT193 699	Craigleith Sandstone, Gullane Formation	
Ballochmyle	Mauchline, Ayrshire	NS499 265	Mauchline Sandstone	
Barnton Park	Edinburgh	NT197 759	? Craigleith Sandstone, Gullane Formation	
Bearford's Parks	Edinburgh	NT 255 740 approx.	Craigleith Sandstone, Gullane Formation	
Binny	Uphall, West Lothian	NT057 730	Binny Sandstone, West Lothian Oil-Shale Formation	
Bishopbriggs (Huntershill and Kenmure)	Bishopbriggs	NS608 695	Bishopbriggs Sandstone, Upper Limestone Formation	
Black Pasture	Hexham, Northumberland	NY931 698	Millstone Grit	Active, Scottish Natural Stones Ltd.
Blair	Culross, Fife	NS966 857	Passage Formation	
Blaxter	Elsdon, Otterburn, Northumberland	NY931 873	Lower Limestone Group (England)	Active, Tynecastle Stone (Haydens Northern)
Braehead	Fauldhouse, West Lothian	NS919 601	Lower Coal Measures	
Broughton	Edinburgh	NT260 745 approx.	Craigleith Sandstone, Gullane Formation	
Burgh Muir (Meadows & Bruntsfield)	Edinburgh	NT 252 725	Kinnesswood Formation	
Carmyllie	Arbroath	NO 546 438	Dundee Formation	
Catcastle	Lartington, Barnard Castle	NZ015 165	Millstone Grit	Active, Dunhouse Quarry Company Ltd.
Clashach	Hopeman, Moray	NJ162 701	Sandstone of Hopeman	Active, Moray Stone Cutters
Closeburn	Thornhill, Dumfries & Galloway	NX892 910	Thornhill Sandstone Formation	
Clunevar	Dunfermline, Fife	NT070 890 approx.	Limestone Coal Formation	
Cocklaw	Chollerford, Northumberland	NY938 703	Middle Limestone Group (England)	
Cockmuir	West Lothian	NT067 765	Binny Sandstone, West Lothian Oil-Shale Formation	
Corncockle	Lochmaben, Dumfries & Galloway	NY086 870	Corncockle Sandstone Formation	Active: Onyx Contractors
Corsehill	Annan, Dumfries & Galloway	NY206 700	St Bees Sandstone Formation	Active: Onyx Contractors
Cragg	Bellingham, Cumbria	NY820 850	Scremerston Coal Group (England)	C & M Stone Products Ltd.

Quarry	Location	NGR	Stratigraphy	Status, operators/owners
Craigcrook (Well Craig, Old Kenny, Stevenson's)	Edinburgh	NT213 742	Craigleith Sandstone, Gullane Formation	
Craigiemill	Edinburgh	NT182 763	Hailes Sandstone, West Lothian Oil-Shale Formation	
Craigleith	Edinburgh	NT226 745	Craigleith Sandstone, Gullane Formation	
Craigmillar	Edinburgh	NT285 709	Kinnesswood Formation	
Craigton	West Lothian	NT076 769	Binny Sandstone, West Lothian Oil-Shale Formation	
Cullalo (several quarries)	Aberdour, Fife	NT184 874	Grange or Cullalo Sandstone, West Lothian Oil-Shale Formation	
Cutties Hillock (Quarry Wood)	Elgin, Moray	NJ185 635	Sandstone of Cutties Hillock	
Dalachy	Burntisland, Fife	NT209 863	Grange Sandstone, West Lothian Oil-Shale Formation	
Dalmeny	West Lothian	NT165 777	Binny Sandstone, West Lothian Oil-Shale Formation	
Darney	West Woodburn, Northumberland	NY910 870	Lower Limestone Group (England)	Active, Natural Stone Products
Denwick	Alnwick, Northumberland	NU210 146	Middle Limestone Group (England)	
Doddington	Wooler, Northumberland	NU008 326	Fell Sandstone Group	Active, Natural Stone Products
Dullatur	Kilsyth	NS741 768	Bishopbriggs Sandstone, Upper Limestone Formation	
Dumbiedykes	Edinburgh	NT265 732	Ballagan Formation	
Dunhouse (or Dunn House)	Staindrop, County Durham	NZ114 195	Millstone Grit	Active, Dunhouse Quarry Company Ltd.
Dunmore (New)	Cowie, Stirling	NS859 882	? Cowie Rock, Upper Limestone Formation	Active, Scottish Natural Stones Ltd.
Dunmore (Old)	Cowie, Stirling	NS838 885	? Cowie Rock, Upper Limestone Formation	
Fairloans	Hawick	NY595 968	Larriston Sandstone, Border Group	
Fordell (possibly Millstonemeadow)	Fife	NT156 849	?Grange Sandstone, West Lothian Oil-Shale Formation	
Gatelawbridge (Newton Quarry)	Thornhill, Dumfries and Galloway	NX902 965	Thornhill Sandstone Formation	Active, Scottish Natural Stones Ltd.
Giffnock, Braidbar Quarries	Glasgow	NS568 593	Giffnock Sandstone, Upper Limestone Formation	
Glanton Pike	Northumberland	NU063 146	Fell Sandstone Group	
Grange	Burntisland, Fife	NT223 867	Grange Sandstone, West Lothian Oil-Shale Formation	
Granton (Land and Sea Quarries)	Edinburgh	NT221 772	Craigleith Sandstone, Gullane Formation	
Greenbrae	Hopeman, Moray	NJ137 692	Sandstones of Hopeman	
Gunnerton	Gunnerton, Northumberland	NY917 764	Middle Limestone Group (England)	

Quarry	Location	NGR	Stratigraphy	Status, operators/owners
Hailes	Edinburgh	NT208 706	Hailes Sandstone, West Lothian Oil-Shale Formation	
Hawkhill Wood	Edinburgh	NT291 711	Kinnesswood Formation	
Hermand	West Calder, West Lothian	NT029 635	Binny Sandstone, West Lothian Oil-Shale Formation	
Heworthburn	Felling, Tyne and Wear	NZ285 616	Middle Coal Measures	
Hopetoun White Quarry	Hopetoun Wood, West Lothian	NT073 773	Binny Sandstone, West Lothian Oil-Shale Formation	
Humbie	West Lothian	NT109 757	Binny Sandstone, West Lothian Oil-Shale Formation	
Humbie, Aberdour	Aberdour, Fife	NT198 862	?Grange Sandstone, West Lothian Oil-Shale Formation	
Joppa	Edinburgh	NT314 730	Upper Limestone Formation	
Lazonby: Stoneraise Quarry	Penrith, Cumbria	NY533 358	Penrith Sandstone Formation	Active: Block Stone Ltd. (Realstone Ltd.) Cumbria Stone Quarries Ltd.
Lazonby Fell Quarry		NY517 380		
Leoch	Tayside	NO359 361	Dundee Formation	
Locharbriggs	Locharbriggs, Dumfries & Galloway	NX990 810	Locharbriggs Sandstone Formation	Active, Baird & Stevenson (Quarrymasters) Ltd.
Longannet	Longannet, Fife	NS950 857	Passage Formation	
Maidencraig (Blackhall; Gibb's Quarry)	Edinburgh	NT223 745	Craigleith Sandstone, Gullane Formation	
Milknock	Bellingham, Northumberland	NY880 794	Scremerston Coal Group (England)	
Moat	Moat, Longtown	NY398 738	St Bees Sandstone Formation	
Myreton	Dundee	NO442 372	Dundee Formation	
Newbigging	Burntisland, Fife	NT211 864	Grange Sandstone, West Lothian Oil-Shale Formation	Active, Scottish Natural Stones Ltd.
Niddrie	Edinburgh	NT308 719	Limestone Coal Formation	
Pasturehill	Northumberland	NU192 293	Lower Limestone Group (England)	
Plean (Blackcraig Quarry)	Stirling	NS825 861	Bishopbriggs Sandstone, Upper Limestone Formation	
Polmaise	Stirling	NS836 892	Cowie Rock, Upper Limestone Formation	
Prudham (& Purdovan)	Fourstones, Hexham, Northumberland	NY886 689	Middle Limestone Group (England)	
Quarry Close	Edinburgh	NT261 730	Gullane Formation	
Quarry Holes (Nether)	Leith	NT270 753	?Ravelston Sandstone, Gullane Formation	
Quarry Holes (Upper)	Edinburgh	NT275 753	Craigleith Sandstone, Gullane Formation	

Quarry	Location	NGR	Stratigraphy	Status, operators/owners
Ravelston Black	Edinburgh	NT212 736	Ravelston Sandstone, Gullane Formation	
Ravelston No.2 (Rosie's Quarry)	Edinburgh	NT214 736	Ravelston Sandstone, Gullane Formation	
Ravelston Quarry (Old), north of Ravelston House	Edinburgh	NT216 742	Craigleith Sandstone, Gullane Formation	
Redhall	Edinburgh	NT215 701	Hailes Sandstone, West Lothian Oil-Shale Formation	
Salisbury: Camstone Quarry	Edinburgh	NT271 734	Ballagan Formation	
Sands	Kincardine	NS949 864	Passage Formation	
Society	Edinburgh	NT257 733	Ballagan Formation	
Spittal No.1	Watten, Caithness	ND172 540	Upper Caithness Flagstone Group	Active, A & D Sutherland
Spittal No.2	Watten, Caithness	ND166 545	Upper Caithness Flagstone Group	Active, Caithness Stone Industries Ltd.
Springwell	Gateshead, Tyne and Wear	NZ283 586	Middle Coal Measures	Active, Natural Stone Quarries Ltd.
Spynie	Elgin, Moray	NJ222 657	Sandstone of Spynie	Active, Moray Stone Cutters
Stainton	County Durham	NZ070 189	Millstone Grit	Active, Natural Stone Products
Stancliffe	Darley Dale, Derbyshire	SK267 638	Millstone Grit	Stancliffe Stone Company Ltd.
Stanton Moor: Palmer's/Dale View New Pillough Birchover	Stanton-in-Peak Stanton-in-Peak Birchover, Matlock	SK249 642 SK249 645 SK242 624	Millstone Grit	Active, Realstone plc Block Stone Ltd. Natural Stone Products, Ennstone plc
Stoke Hall	Eyam, Derbyshire	SK237 770	Millstone Grit	Active, Stoke Hall Quarry Ltd.
Stonegunn	Castletown, Caithness	ND157 659	Upper Caithness Flagstone Group	Active, Caithness Stone Industries Ltd.
Straiton	Edinburgh	NT274 665	West Lothian Oil-Shale Formation	
Swinton	Greenlaw, Berwickshire	NT853 484	Cementstone Group	
Wattscliffe	Elton, Matlock	SK222 622	Millstone Grit	Active, Block Stone Ltd (Realstone Ltd.)
Wellfield (Crossland Hill)	Crossland Hill, Huddersfield, West Yorkshire	SE118 143	Rough Rock, Millstone Grit	Active, Johnsons Wellfield Quarries Ltd.
Whitsome Newton	Greenlaw, Berwickshire	NT854 486	Cementstone Group	
Woodburn (also Parkhead)	West Woodburn, Northumberland	NY902 858	Lower Limestone Group (England)	
Woodkirk	Morley, Yorkshire	SE268 263	Middle Coal Measures	Active, Pawson Brothers Ltd.

APPENDIX 3 Quarry sources for Edinburgh's buildings

Buildings are listed in alphabetical order. Map numbers refer to Figure 1.1. Dates are the latest documented use of stone in the building.

Map No.	Building name and address	Construction repair	Completion date	Quarry source
187	Abbotsford Bar, north side of Rose Street	Construction	1902	Gatelawbridge
	Alma Lodge, Midmar Drive	Construction	pre-1940	Braehead
	Annandale Street, Nos. 6-10	Repairs	1998	Stanton Moor
152	Apex House, Haddington Place/Annandale Street	Construction	1975	Springwell
51	Arden Street area	Construction	1911	Blaxter
				Denwick
30	Art College, Lauriston Place	Construction	1910	Closeburn
	Extension	Construction	1972	Locharbriggs
2	Balmoral (formerly North British) Hotel, east end of Princes Street	Construction	1902	Prudham
		Repairs	1991	Dunhouse
101	Bank of Scotland, 66 George Street	Construction	1876	Dalmeny
106	Bank of Scotland, 103 George Street	Construction	1885	Hermand
123	Bank of Scotland, 38 St Andrew Square	Construction	1846	Binny
13	Bank of Scotland, The Mound	Construction	1806	Binny
		Paving		Carmyllie
		Indents	1986	Stainton
	Barony Street, Nos. 1-13	Repairs	1985	Stainton
	Baxters Place, Stevenson House	Repairs	1980	Darney
	Bellevue Terrace, Nos. 4-9	Repairs	1974	Blaxter
	Bonnington Road School, Leith	Construction	1875	Grange
53	Boroughmuir Secondary School, Viewforth	Construction	1911	Hailes
		Dressings		Doddington
	Braid Church, Nile Grove	Construction	1886	Prudham
				Hailes ('grey')
99	British Home Stores, 64 Princes Street	Construction	1965	Wellfield
1	British Rail, Waverley extensions, North Bridge	Construction	1895	Woodburn
				Sands
154	Broughton Primary School	Construction	1897	Hailes
	Broughton Street, Nos. 47-53/Forth Street	Repairs	1998	Stanton Moor
148	Broughton Street/Albany Street Office Development	Construction	1983	Stainton
153	Brunswick House, Brunswick Street	Construction	1975	Woodkirk
42	Buccleuch and Greyfriars Free Church, West Crosscauseway	Indents	1986	Stainton
155	Buchanan Street Lane	Construction		Dunhouse
142	Burns' Monument, Calton Hill	Construction	1830	Humbie (West Lothian)
		Indents	1978	Darney
166	Burtons, 30-31 Princes Street (formerly R W Forsyth)	Construction	1907	Blaxter
121	Bus Station (offices above entrance), No. 31 St Andrew Square	Construction	1970	Prudham
119	C & A Store, 33-38 Princes Street	Construction	1956	Woodkirk

Map No.	Building name and address	Construction repair	Completion date	Quarry source
65	Caledonian Hotel, West End (Plate 11)	Construction	1903	Corncockle Locharbriggs
	Calton Hill, Nos. 20-26	Repairs	1998	Stainton Stancliffe Stanton Moor
	Candlish Church Tower, Polwarth Terrace	Construction	1913	Closeburn Hailes
143	Canongate redevelopment, Nos. 202-254	Construction	1966	Clashach
60	Capital House, Lothian Road	Construction	1985	Woodkirk
24	Central Library, George IV Bridge	Construction	1890	Polmaise
55	Fat Sams (formerly Central Meat Market), West Fountainbridge	Construction	1890	Corncockle
34	Charity Workhouse, Forrest Hill (part only surviving)	Construction	1743	City
20	Charles II Statue pedestal, Parliament Square	Plinth	1835	Craigleith
91	Charlotte Square, north side (Figure 6.1g)	Construction	1795 after 1805	Craigleith Redhall
	Charlotte Street tenements, Leith	Construction	1870	Grange
185	Chessels Court, Canongate	Construction	1969	Clashach
83	Cheyne Street, Nos. 15-19	Refacing	1984	Dunhouse
	The Church of the Good Shepherd, Murrayfield Avenue	Construction	1897	Hailes
17	City Art Centre, Market Street	Construction	1902 1979	Prudham Woodburn
15	City Chambers, High Street	Construction Additions Construction	1761 1904	Craigleith Longannet Prudham
	Cockburn Street extension	Construction	1934	Darney
	City Hospital, Greenbank Drive	Construction	1903	Closeburn
138	City Observatory House, Calton Hill	Dressings Rubble	1792	Craigleith Local volcanic rock and sandstone
138	City Observatory, Calton Hill	Construction Additions	1818 1895	Craigleith Binny
	Cluny Gardens, No. 1	Construction	1880	Corsehill Hailes ('pink')
67	Coates Crescent	Ashlar	c. 1820	Hailes
71	Coates Gardens	Construction	1876	Dalmeny
16	Cockburn Street	Construction	1864	Bishopbriggs
	Coltbridge Hall, Coltbridge Terrace, Murrayfield (St George's School)	Construction	1874	Dunmore
	Comiston Drive, villas at the west end	Construction	pre-1940	Braehead
	Corstorphine Old Parish Church, Kirk Loan	Reconstruction Internal restoration	1646 1905	Ravelston Prudham
	Figures & War Memorial	Interior	1923	Ravelston No. 2

Map No.	Building name and address	Construction repair	Completion date	Quarry source
	Craigcrook Castle	Additions	1891	Craigton
	Craigcrook Road, bungalows and villas	Construction	1939	Ravelston No. 2
	Craighall Gardens, villas	Construction	1899	Prudham
	Craigmillar Castle	Construction	late 15th century	Craigmillar
141	Crown Office Buildings, Calton Hill (former Royal High School)	Construction	1829	Craigleith
26	Crown Office, Chambers Street (formerly Heriot-Watt University)	Construction	1886	Prudham
57	Dalry Primary School, Dalry Road	Construction	1877	Hailes
80	Daniel Stewart and Melville College, Queensferry Road	Construction	1848	Binny
14	David Hume Statue, High Street	Plinth	1997	Clashach
77	Dean Bridge	Construction	1832	Craigleith
78	Dean Cemetery Wall	Dressed work Rubble work	1915	Woodburn Hailes
	Dean Terrace, No. 16	Repairs	1998	Stanton Moor
94	Debenham's, 109-112 Princes Street	Construction above street level	1884	Polmaise
94	Debenham's, Rose Street	Construction	1884	Hermand
	Dewar Place	?Repairs	1998	Stoke Hall
	Dick Place	Construction	1865	City
98	Dolcis, 70 Princes Street	Construction	1886	Corsehill
103	Dome Bar (formerly Royal Bank of Scotland), 14 George Street	Construction	1847	Binny
73	Donaldson's School for the Deaf, West Coates	Construction	1851	Binny
74	Drumsheugh Gardens, Nos. 42 and 43	Construction	1877	Polmaise
	Duddingston Kirk, Old Church Lane	Construction	17th century	Craigmillar
137	Dugald Stewart Monument, Calton Hill	Construction	1831	Humbie (West Lothian)
		Pillars	1997	?
	Dundas Street, Nos. 18-20	Repairs	1998	Stanton Moor
	Dynamic Earth, Holyrood Road	Construction	1999	Stanton Moor
149	East Broughton Place Church Hall	Dressings	1887	Corsehill
	East Hermitage Place, Nos. 9-11, Leith	Construction	1883	Dalmeny
85	The Edinburgh Academy, Henderson Row	Construction	1824	Craigleith Cullalo Hailes Redhall
	The Edinburgh Academy, Jeffrey and Scott Boarding Houses, Kinnear Road	Dressings	1899	Corncockle Locharbriggs
9	Edinburgh Castle and The Shrine (17th to 20th century)	Construction	1616 1619 1628 1639	St Cuthbert's Craigleith Maidencraig Craigmillar
		Restoration	1978	Clashach
	Hall of Honour, National War Memorial	Construction	1927	Doddington Swinton

Map No.	Building name and address	Construction repair	Completion date	Quarry source
	Edinburgh reservoirs, various	Construction	1822-1880	Craigmillar
174	Edinburgh Solicitors Property Centre, 85 George Street	Construction	1990	Gatelawbridge (Newton)
	Elm Row, Nos. 20-23	Repairs	1998	Stancliffe
147	Elsie Inglis Hospital, Spring Gardens	Construction	1923	Cullalo
	Esslemont Road villas	Rubble Facework	1920	Hawkhill Wood Doddington Braehead
161	Exchange Plaza, Lothian Road	Construction	1997	Dunhouse
	Eyre Crescent, Nos. 28-29	Repairs	1998	Stanton Moor
	Fairmilehead Parish Church, Frogston Road/ Comiston Road	Construction Ashlar	1938	Hawkhill Wood Doddington
81	Fettes College, East Fettes Avenue	Construction	1870	Cullalo
87	Fettes Row, Nos. 30-31	Facing	1974	Clashach
59	Film House, Lothian Road	Construction	1831	Redhall
160	Fire Station, Lauriston Place	Construction	1901	Locharbriggs
86	First Church of Christ Scientist, Inverleith Terrace	Construction	1911	Cullalo
	Forres Street No. 11/Moray Place	Repairs	1998	Blaxter
56	Fountainbridge Telephone Exchange, Gardners Crescent	Construction	1952	Blaxter
165	Frasers Department Store, Nos. 145-149 Princes Street	Construction	1935	Heworthburn
159	Free Church of Scotland College, Mound Place	Construction	1863	Hailes ('blue')
92	Freemasons' Hall — St Andrew Statue 96 George Street	Above plinth	1912	Pasturehill
	Gardiner Road, bungalows and villas	Construction	1939	Ravelston No. 2
	Gayfield Place, Nos. 21-23 Nos. 24-26 Nos. 30-32 No. 33	Repairs	1998	Stancliffe Stanton Moor Stanton Moor Stancliffe
66	General Accident Assurance, Canning Lane, West End and 1-8 Atholl Crescent	Construction	1985	Dunhouse
132	General Post Office (former), east end of Princes Street	Construction	1866 1890 & 1909	Binny Doddington
33	George Heriot's School, Lauriston Place Interior courtyard Additions	Construction Rubble	1700 1700 1920	Ravelston Craigleith Craigmillar Hawkhill Wood
45	George Square, surviving early buildings, east side: No. 60 (north-east corner of the square)	Construction Rubble	1779	Craigleith Craigmillar with dolerite blocks
44	George Square Theatre	Construction	1967	Wellfield
43	George Square, few surviving buildings, west side: Most of the surviving buildings (including no. 20, Plate 3)	Construction Course squared rubble	1775	Craigleith Craigmillar with dolerite snecks

Map No.	Building name and address	Construction repair	Completion date	Quarry source
104	George Street, No. 2	Construction	1966	Heworthburn
173	George Street, No. 10	Construction	1990	Catcastle
93	George Street, No. 26, Royal Society of Edinburgh (former Commercial Union building)	Construction	1909	Portland Stone (limestone)
102	George Street, Nos. 40-42	Construction	1984	Stainton
108	George Street, No. 45	Construction	1974	Darney
107	George Street, No. 65	Construction	1908	Doddington
100	George Street, No. 68	Construction	1955	Blaxter
175	George Street, No. 97	Restoration Central portico and indents	1980	Clashach Stainton
	George Watson's College, Colinton Road War Memorial	Construction	1930	Doddington Cullalo
134	Governor's House, Calton Gaol	Construction	1817	Hermand
	Grange Loan villas	Construction	late 19th century	Braehead
	Grant Institute of Geology, The University of Edinburgh, King's Buildings, West Mains Road	Construction	1931	Blaxter
	Granton Harbour	Construction	1838	Granton
	Granton Old Parish Church, Granton Road (disused)	Construction	1877	Fordell
	Granton Parish Church, Boswall Parkway	Construction	1934	Craigmillar Doddington
	Great Junction Street tenements, Leith, Nos. 69 and 71	Construction	1884	Dalmeny
	Great King Street, Nos. 37-41	Repairs	1998	Stanton Moor
169	Great King Street, Nos. 83-89	Mouldings	1982	Spynie
	Great Michael Home & Links House (formerly Scottish Co-operative Wholesale Society), Leith Links	Construction	1879	Polmaise
	North-eastern extension		1885	Plean
	Great Stuart Street, No. 16	Repairs	1985	Stancliffe
	Haddington Place, Nos. 1-8	Repairs	1998	Blaxter Stancliffe
	Hamilton Place, Nos. 6-10	Repairs	1985	Stancliffe
	Nos. 84-92		1998	Stanton Moor
	Hanover Street, Nos. 91-95	Repairs		Blaxter
	Henderson Row, Nos. 109-119	Repairs	1998	Stancliffe Stanton Moor
	Henderson Street tenements, Leith	Construction	1888	Doddington
88	Heriot Row	Construction	c. 1808	Redhall
	No. 35	Repairs	1998	Stanton Moor
14	High Court of Justiciary, Bank Street	Construction	1937	Darney
79	Hilton National Hotel, Belford Road	Construction	1978	Woodkirk

Map No.	Building name and address	Construction repair	Completion date	Quarry source
	Historic Scotland, Longmore House, Salisbury Place	Interior floor		Ledmore (marble)
183	Holiday Inn Crowne Plaza Hotel, High Street (formerly Scandic Crown Hotel)	Rubble and dressed work	1990	Dunhouse
146	Holyrood Palace (mainly 16th century)	Construction	16th century	Barnbougle Broughton Craigleith Cramond Dumbiedykes Granton Leith Hill Niddrie Queensferry Ravelston St Cuthbert's Stenhouse
			1616	Craigmillar Salisbury
		Paving and steps	1983	Spittal Wellfield
	Fountain	Construction	1859	Binny
168	Howe Street, No. 39	Mouldings	1982	Spynie
	India Street, Nos. 8-12	Repairs	1998	Stanton Moor
	Nos. 17, 19 and 21			Dunhouse
164	International Conference Centre, Morrison Street	Construction	1996	Stoke Hall
105	Jenner's, Princes Street	Construction	1895	Cragg
105	Jenner's, Rose Street	Construction	1890	Gatelawbridge
177	John Lewis extension, Leith Walk	Cladding		Stainton
157	King's Theatre, Tollcross	Construction	1904	Closeburn
182	Lady Glenorchy's Church, Roxburgh Place	Construction	1913	Cullalo
	Landsdowne Crescent, No. 3	Repairs	1998	Stanton Moor
31	Lauriston Place, ground floor	Repairs	1981	Woodkirk
	Lawnmarket, north side tenements	Construction	1690s	Burgh Muir (Bruntsfield) and Craigmillar
	Leith Academy Annexe, Lochend Road	Construction	1887	Corncockle Hailes
	Leith Bulwark	Construction	1555	Burgh Muir Granton
	Leith Docks	Construction	1876 1896	Craigleith Craigmillar
	Leith Town Hall, Constitution Street	Construction	1827	Craigleith
171	Leslie Place, No. 12	Indents	1982	Spynie
150	London Street School	Construction	1887	Prudham
	London Street, Nos. 5-9 Nos. 11-13	Repairs	1998	Stanton Moor

Map No.	Building name and address	Construction repair	Completion date	Quarry source
58	Lothian House, Lothian Road — including stone relief of a canal barge	Construction	1936	Blaxter
	Luckenbooths, tenements	Construction	1741	Burgh Muir (Bruntsfield)
72	Magdala Crescent	Construction	1876	Dalmeny
151	Mansfield Place Church (formerly Bellevue Reformed Baptist Church), East London Street	Construction	1885	Plean Woodburn
50	Marchmont Crescent, No. 38 (tenement)	Construction	1881	Clunevar
95	Marks and Spencer, 104 Princes Street	Construction	1980	Dunhouse
	Mayfield Road villas	Rubble Facework	1920	Hawkhill Wood Doddington Braehead
37	McEwan Hall, Teviot Place (Plate 8)	Construction Columns (2nd floor)	1897	Polmaise Prudham Corsehill
158	Meadows West Commemorative Pillars and Sundial, West Meadow Park, Melville Drive (Figures 6.2-6.3)	Individual ashlar blocks	1886	Ballochmyle Binny Cocklaw Corncockle Corsehill Cragg Dalmeny Dunmore Gatelawbridge Gunnerton Hailes Hermand Leoch Moat Myreton Parkhead – (Woodburn) Plean Polmaise Prudham Redhall Whitsome – Newton Woodburn
36	Medical School, Teviot Place	Construction	1886	Polmaise
117	Melville Monument, St Andrew Square	Construction	1823	Cullalo
19	Mercat Cross, Parliament Square	Restoration	1885	Hermand
89	Merchant's Hall, 22 Hanover Street	Construction	1866 1901	Dullatur Prudham
	Merchiston Crescent, tenements	Construction	1888	Cragg
54	Methodist Central Hall, Tollcross	Construction	1901	Doddington
144	Milton House School, Canongate	Construction	1886	Corncockle Hailes ('grey')

Map No.	Building name and address	Construction repair	Completion date	Quarry source
184	Moray House Teacher Training College, Holyrood Road	Repairs	1970	Clashach
	Moray Place, No. 14	Repairs	1998	Stanton Moor
	Morningside tenements	Construction	1885	Gunnerton
	Mound Place, tenements	Construction	late 18th century	Burgh Muir (Bruntsfield) and Craigmillar
	Murrayfield Parish Church, Abinger Gardens	Construction	1905	Hailes Prudham
27	Museum of Scotland, Chambers Street, (Plate 12)	Cladding	1998	Clashach
	Napier University, Merchiston Tower, No. 10 Colinton Road	Construction Later work	c.15th century	Burgh Muir Hailes Ravelston
		Restoration	1958	Doddington
156	National Gallery of Modern Art (formerly John Watson's School), Belford Road	Construction	1825	Craigleith
5	National Gallery, The Mound (Plate 6)	Construction	1859	Binny
47	National Library of Scotland, 33 Salisbury Place, Causewayside	Construction Phase II	1987 1994	Newbigging Newbigging
22	National Library of Scotland, George IV Bridge	Construction	1955	Blaxter
140	National Monument, Calton Hill (Detail: Figure 2.8)	Construction	1829	Craigleith
114	National Portrait Gallery, Queen Street	Construction	1890	Corsehill Moat
139	Nelson Monument, Calton Hill	Construction	1816	Craigleith
12	New College and Assembly Hall, The Mound	Construction Paving and steps	1850	Binny Hailes Carmyllie
127	New Register House, West Register Street, east end	Construction	1863	Longannet
	New Restalrig Parish Church, Willowbrae Road	Construction	1890	Corsehill
41	Nicolson Street Church (Civic Centre)	Indents and repairs	1986	Stainton
40	Nicolson Street, No. 82 (Figure 2.9)	Rubble work	late 18th century	Salisbury (dolerite)
	North Bridge	Construction	1773	Maidencraig
	North Junction Street, Leith	Construction	1891	Clunevar
	North Morningside (United Presbyterian) Church, Chamberlain Road	Construction	1881	Dunmore Polmaise
179	Norwich Union Insurance Group, 32 St Andrew Square	Construction	1970	Prudham
28	Old College, The University of Edinburgh Dome	Construction Construction	1827 1879	Craigleith Grange
118	Old Waverley Hotel, 43 Princes Street	Construction	1887	Cragg

Map No.	Building name and address	Construction repair	Completion date	Quarry source
	Oxgangs Road, houses	Construction	1930	Locharbriggs
70	Palmerston Place Church, west side	Construction	1875	Polmaise
68	Palmerston Place, east side	Construction	1880s	Dalmeny
	Nos. 15-21	Indents	1985	Dunhouse
				Stancliffe
21	Parliament House, High Street	Freestone	1639	Burgh Muir
				Ravelston
		Rubble	1633	Society
		Façade	1810	Craigleith
176	Paton Building/York Place, Nos. 1-3 (Plate 14)	Restoration	1998	Clashach
	Prince Regent Street tenements, Leith	Construction	1882	Grange
97	Princes Street, Nos. 91-93	Construction	1960	Heworthburn
	Prudential Assurance, 2 St Andrew Square	Construction	1895	Locharbriggs
172	Queen Street, No. 8	Construction	1771	Craigleith
186	Queen Street, Nos. 2-3	Construction		Prudham
76	Randolph Cliff tenement, northern corner	Construction	1849	Craigleith
75	Randolph Crescent	Construction	1820s	Redhall
	Redford Barracks, Colinton Road	Hewn work	1915	Black Pasture
		Rubble		Doddington
	Redhall Bank Road, Nos. 8-10 (quarrymen's cottages)	Construction	1850s	Redhall
131	Regent Bridge, arch	Construction	1815	Craigmillar
128	Register House, east end of Princes Street	Construction	1778	Craigleith
				Hailes
		Gallery construction	1789	Craigleith
		Paving		Hailes
		Construction	1820s	Craigleith
		Paving		Carmyllie
				Hailes
		Construction	1834	? Binny
	Reid Memorial Church, West Savile Terrace	Ashlar	1933	Doddington
		Rubble		Hawkhill Wood
		Roofing		Caithness
				Flagstones
	Roseburn Primary School, Roseburn Street (Plate 5)	Squared rubble	1893	Hailes ('pink' and 'blue')
		Dressings		Corsehill
	Roseburn Terrace tenements	Construction	1882	Clunevar
				Auchinlea
	Ross Road villas	Facework	1920	Braehead
		Rubble		Hawkhill Wood
122	Royal Bank of Scotland (formerly National Bank of Scotland), No. 42 St Andrew Square	Construction	1936	Darney
		Base		Rubislaw (granite)
39	Royal Bank of Scotland, Nicolson Street	Construction	1902	Corncockle

Map No.	Building name and address	Construction repair	Completion date	Quarry source
124	Royal Bank of Scotland, No. 36 St Andrew Square	Construction	1774	Ravelston
167	Royal Crescent, Nos. 8-11	Restoration	1979	Springwell
46	Royal Dick School of Veterinary Studies, Summerhall	Dressings Rubble work	1916	Doddington Hailes
35	Royal Infirmary, Lauriston Place Jubilee Pavilion Extensions	Construction Construction Construction	1879 1897	Hailes Corsehill Cullalo Longannet
	Simpson Maternity Pavilion	Construction	1935	Blaxter
27	Royal Museum of Scotland, Chambers Street Figures West wing Extension to south Lecture Theatre, Lothian Street	Indents Sculptures Construction Construction Construction	1986 1861 1889 1934 1961	Stainton Doddington Hermand Cullalo Blaxter
	Royal Observatory, Blackford Hill Extensions	Construction Construction	1892 1967	Doddington Hailes Woodkirk
96	Royal Overseas League, 100 Princes Street (formerly Windsor Hotel)	Construction	1880	Dalmeny
6	Royal Scots Monument, West Princes Street Gardens	Construction	1950	Doddington
4	Royal Scottish Academy, The Mound (Plate 7)	Construction	1826	Cullalo Craigleith Binny
		Additions	1836	Humbie (West Lothian)
	Queen Victoria Statue	Sculpture	1844	Binny
49	Royal Sick Children's Hospital, Sciennes Road	Construction	1892	Corsehill
110	St Andrew's and St George's Church, George Street	Ashlar Columns	1784	Redhall Craigleith
115	St Andrew Square oldest buildings, Nos. 21, 22, 26	Construction	1772	Bearford's Parks
178	St Andrew Square, No. 9, upper elevations: Street level:	Cladding	1962	Derbydene limestone Bon Accord (black granite)
116	St Andrew Square, No. 28 and North St David Street (west side) (formerly Scottish Equitable Assurance) (Plate 9)	Construction	1899	Doddington
180	St Andrew Square, No. 35	Construction	1781	Craigleith
135	St Andrew's House, Calton Hill	Construction	1939	Darney
	St Anne's Church, St John's Road, Corstorphine	Rock faced Columns	1912	Hailes('pink') Cullalo
	St Anne's Church Hall, Corstorphine	Construction	1928	Craigmillar

Map No.	Building name and address	Construction repair	Completion date	Quarry source
	St Anthony's Chapel, Arthur's Seat	Rubble	Late medieval	Local volcanic rocks
170	St Bernards Crescent, No. 1a	Indents	1982	Spynie
18	St Giles Cathedral (High Kirk), High Street	Facing	1833	Cullalo
		Interior	1911	Cullalo
	Access to undercroft	Interior access	1984	Lazonby
	St James Episcopal Church, Inverleith Row	Construction	1885	Corsehill
	St James Square, Nos. 23-26	Repairs	1998	Stanton Moor
8	St John's, Princes Street	Construction	1818	Redhall
		Indents		Stainton
69	St Mary's Cathedral School	Construction	1885	Hermand
69	St Mary's Cathedral, Palmerston Place	Construction	1917	Cullalo
	Spire	Construction	1917	Black Pasture
129	St Mary's Roman Catholic Cathedral.	? repairs	1891	Purdovan
	Broughton Street	Repairs	1978	Woodkirk
181	St Mary's Street, No. 32	Restoration	1983	Stanton Moor
130	St Paul's and St George's Episcopal Church	Construction	1818	Redhall
	St Stephen Street, Nos. 20-60	Refacing	1980	Darney
84	St Stephen's Church, St Vincent Street	Construction	1828	Craigleith
82	St Stephen's Comely Bank Parish Church,	Construction	1901	Corsehill
	10 Comely Bank Road			Hailes
	St Vincent Street, Nos. 10-14	Repairs	1998	Stainton
				Stancliffe
	Nos. 16-18a		1981	Darney
	Sainsbury's plc Supermarket, Queensferry Road, entrance façade	Construction	1993	Stainton
63	Saltire Court, Castle Terrace	Construction	1991	Stainton
	(Plate 10)			Gatelawbridge (Newton)
48	Sciennes Primary School, Sciennes Road	Construction	1889	Hailes
3	The Scott Monument, Princes Street	Construction	1846	Binny
		Indents	1975	Clashach
10	Scotch Whisky Heritage Centre (formerly	Margins	1896	Corncockle
	Castlehill School)	Rock face ashlar		Hailes ('blue')
	Scotland Street, Nos. 29-31a	Repairs	1979	Darney
17	Scotsman Offices, North Bridge	Construction	1902	Prudham
				Woodburn
145	Scottish & Newcastle plc, 111 Holyrood Road	Construction	1961	Blaxter
112	Scottish Life Assurance Company,	Construction	1962	Springwell
	2 North St David Street			Wellfield
		Entrance columns		Larvikite (Norway)
163	Scottish Widows Fund and Life Assurance Society Morrison Street (Plate 13)	Construction	1997	Clashach

Map No.	Building name and address	Construction repair	Completion date	Quarry source
7	Scottish/American War Memorial, West Princes Street Gardens	Construction	1927	Ravelston No. 2
	Seafield Lodge	Construction	1888	Grange
61	Sheraton Hotel, Lothian Road (front only)	Construction	1985	Wellfield
23	Sheriff Court House, 27-29 Chambers Street	Construction	1997	Catcastle
155	South Buchanan Street, tenements	Construction	1881	Auchinlea
126	South St Andrew Street, No. 7	Construction	1886	Cragg
125	South St Andrew Street, Nos. 11-13, Job Centre	Construction		Wellfield
120	South St Andrew Street, Nos. 10-18 York Place	Construction	1915	Blaxter
111	Standard Life Assurance extension, Thistle Street	Construction Entrance paving	1964	Blaxter Spittal
162	Standard Life, Lothian Road	Construction	1997	Stainton
113	Stock Exchange, North St David Street	Construction	1970s	Stainton
38	Surgeons Hall, Nicolson Street	Construction	1832	Craigton Cullalo Humbie (West Lothian)
	Thistle Foundation, Robin Chapel, Niddrie Mains Road	Construction	1953	Doddington
11	Tolbooth St John's Church, Lawnmarket	Construction	1844	Binny
133	Trinity College Church, Chalmers Close (15th-16th century, rebuilt on present site 1872)	Construction	1872	Bearford's Parks
	Trinity villas	Construction	1883	Auchinlea Ravelston
25	Tron Kirk, High Street	Construction Repairs	1647 1787 1976	Society Craigleith Craigleith Craigleith Darney
	Spire	Construction	1828	Humbie (West Lothian)
109	Trustee Savings Bank, George Street, Nos. 120-124	Facing Paving in the entrance hall and atrium	1986	Dunmore (new) Ross of Mull (pink granite)
	Turnhouse Airport Terminal	Construction	1954	Auchinlea
	Tynecastle School Annexe, Gorgie Road	Construction	1876	Redhall
	Union Street, Nos. 10-12a/Forth Street	Repairs	1998	Stanton Moor
62	Unitarian Church, Castle Terrace	Construction	1835	Cullalo
	United Distillers, Distillers House, 33 Ellersly Road	Construction	1981	Wellfield
64	Usher Hall, Lothian Road	Construction	1914	Darney Leoch

Map No.	Building name and address	Construction repair	Completion date	Quarry source
32	Vennel area, Bastion and Flodden Wall Figure 6.1a)	Construction	16th century	Burgh Muir Ravelston Hailes
	Victoria Primary School, Newhaven Main Street	Construction	1884	Grange
52	Warrender Park Crescent, Nos. 1-8	Construction	1881	Blair
136	Waterloo Place, columns	Construction	1815	Craigleith
29	West Port Church (no longer a church)	Construction	1844	Hermand
90	West Register House — formerly St George's Church, Charlotte Square	Construction	1814	Craigleith
	Westerlea School, Ellersly Road	Construction	1869	Dullatur
	Western General Hospital, Surgical Neurology Building: Radiotherapy Building:	Construction	1952 1956	Blaxter Blaxter
	Yardheads School, Giles Street, Leith	Construction	1887	Gunnerton
	Zoology Department, The University of Edinburgh, King's Buildings, West Mains Road	Construction	1929	Blaxter

APPENDIX 4 Dates of operation and peak numbers employed in selected sandstone quarries

Quarry	Date of earliest reference	Peak numbers employed when published	Remarks — date of last reference (Quarry List/Directory)
Auchinlea, Motherwell (2 quarries)	1878	150 (1895); North Auchinlea 162	Almost continuous N. Auchinlea Closed after 1914
Barnton Park, Edinburgh	Before 1880 but not on first O.S. map 1853	30 (1901)	1916
Binny, Uphall, West Lothian (3 quarries in 1858)	1794	30 (1806); 22 (1895)	By 1899 only used for monumental purposes
Bishopbriggs, Glasgow (Huntershill)	1854 (mine)	5 quarries in 1858 and mining (46 men) in 1905	Not listed after 1907 when mine closed after 5 men killed by roof fall
Blair, Culross, Fife	1835		1877: not in 1895 List
Blaxton, Elsdon, Northumberland	1878 (8 men)	95 (1925)	Active
Braehead, Fauldhouse, West Lothian	1897 (38 men)	57 (1899)	1937
Burgh Muir (Meadows and Bruntsfield), Edinburgh (many small workings including the City Quarry)	1554		Last recorded 1741; City Quarry still visible
Catcastle, Lartington, Barnard Castle	Pre-1900		1914, re-opened 1977; active
Clashach, Hopeman, Moray	1860	28 (1901)	Intermittent after 1937: re-opened 1963-64; active
Clunevar, Dunfermline, Fife	1881	14 (1895)	1897
Corncockle, Lochmaben, Dumfries & Galloway	1824	124 (1898)	Last listed 1955-56; re-opened 1986; active
Corsehill, Annan, Dumfries & Galloway	1880	241 (1916)	Last listed 1955-56; re-opened 1981; active
Cragg, Bellingham, Northumberland	1886		Listed 1895
Craigleith, Edinburgh	1616 (deserted in late 18th century)	91 (1895)	Intermittent after 1905; used for rubble, glass-cutting, concrete aggregate, road bottoming; infilled and redeveloped by Sainsbury's plc. Site is a proposed RIGS

Quarry	Date of earliest reference	Peak numbers employed when published	Remarks — date of last reference (Quarry List/Directory)
Craigmillar, Edinburgh (at least 4 quarries)	1374 (Craigmillar Castle) 1531 (Edinburgh Castle)	21 (1937)	Intermittent after 1906; some quarries infilled; Hawkhill Wood worked 1922-40
Craigton, Philpstoun, West Lothian	1890		One of the quarries worked until 1933
Cullalo, Fife (several quarries)	1822	50 (1898)	Intermittent; last 1948
Dalmeny, Queensferry	1874		Said to be "practically worked out" 1892
Darney, West Woodburn, Northumberland	1910	85 (1937)	1948
Denwick, Alnwick, Northumberland	1895	80 (1902)	1937
Doddington, Wooler, Northumberland	1887	30 (1911-12)	Still listed 1973
Dullatur, Kilsyth	1860s	71 (1903)	As stone quarry stopped 1920s; sand quarry into 1930s
Dunhouse, Staindrop, County Durham	Early 1900s		Active
Dunmore, Stirling	Pre-1855	55 (1895)	Closed after 1906; new Dunmore Quarry opened 1985.
Fordell, Fife	1878	15 (1907)	Only listed one year in Quarry Returns
Gatelawbridge, Dumfries & Galloway	c. 17th century	108 (1905)	After 1912 intermittent until 1925; Newton Quarry re-opened 1986
Grange, Burntisland, Fife	1837	110 (1902)	1914
Granton, Edinburgh (several quarries, e.g. 2 in 1858)	1531; 1831 (Granton Point)	19 (1902): Pennywell; 23 (1922): Royston	"Granton Point" flooded 1855; Pennywell Parks 1903; Royston 1925
Gunnerton, Northumberland	1885	70 (1897)	1914; intermittent after 1909
Hailes, Edinburgh	Early 1600s	225 (1899)	Building stone to 1920; mudstone to 1943-44
Hermand, West Calder, West Lothian	1883	14 (1896)	1896
Heworthburn, Felling, Tyne and Wear	1831	55 (1913)	Active
Hopetoun White, Hopetoun Wood, West Lothian (3 quarries operated simultaneously)	1697	27 (1902)	3 quarries at times; little work after 1908
Humbie, Winchburgh, West Lothian	1791	80 (1835)	2 quarries 1858; not working 1869 (flooded)
Lazonby, Penrith (several quarries)	Pre-1900		Active

Quarry	Date of earliest reference	Peak numbers employed when published	Remarks — date of last reference (Quarry List/Directory)
Locharbriggs, Dumfries & Galloway	c. 1700	267 (1899)	Active
Longannet, Stirlingshire	1791	155 (1910)	1910
Maidencraig, Edinburgh (Blackhall)	1628		In use late 18th century; flooded by 1855
Moat, Longtown	1856	61 (1898)	1918
Newbigging, Burntisland, Fife	1856	30 (1896)	Intermittent after 1914; closed 1937; re-opened 1980 and 1984
Pasturehill, Northumberland	1909	40 (1911)	1914
Plean, Stirlingshire (several quarries)	1885 (said to have opened about 1860)	31 (1902)	1912
Polmaise, Stirling	1877 (said to have opened about 1860)	38 (1897)	Closed in 1892 when said to be almost worked out; intermittent after 1910; closed after 1931
Prudham, Fourstones, Northumberland	1850	106 (1896, 1904, 1907)	1914
Purdovan, Northumberland	1891		not listed 1895
Ravelston, Edinburgh (several quarries)	1511	28 (1920)	Ravelston No. 2 last listed 1939
Redhall, Edinburgh (2 quarries latterly)	1657	15 (1834)	Intermittent to last building, 1876; used in Meadows Pillars 1886; not listed 1895
Sands, Kincardine, Stirling	1835	5 (1899)	1899
Springwell, Gateshead, Tyne and Wear	1872	53 (1931)	Active
Stainton, Durham (several quarries)	1858	8 (1937)	Active
Stancliffe, Darley Dale, Matlock	Worked for at least 100 years		Active
Stanton Moor (Palmers Quarry), Stanton-in-Peak	1945		Re-opened 1983; active
Stoke Hall, Grindleford, Derbyshire	1835		Active
Swinton, Greenlaw, Berwickshire	1791	11 (1901)	1920
Wellfield, West Yorkshire	1901	52 (1925)	Active
Woodburn, Northumberland	1886 (said to have been introduced about 1882)	66 (1900)	1908; then said to have been intermittent until 1922
Woodkirk, Morley Yorkshire	Worked since the 1930s		Active

Little-known early Edinburgh quarries

Quarry	Date of earliest reference	Date of last reference	Remarks
Barnbougle	1535		
Bearford's Quarries (Nor Loch)	1701	1770	
Broughton	1622		
Cramond	1535	1536	
Leith Hill	1529	1529	
Niddrie	1529	1536	Standing 1839; open 1858; not listed 1895
Quarry Close	1734		Reference to 7 years' lease
Quarry Holes	Very early	1677 disused	
St Cuthbert's	1615	1786	
Salisbury (Camstone & Dolerite)	1529	1821	
"Society" (possibly one of the Greyfriars Port quarries)	1533	1654	20 men and labourers in 1632
Stenhouse (Liberton)	1531	1532	
Wardie	1657	1657	

APPENDIX 5 Properties of building stones: A. Comparative table of data

Quarry	Bulk Density kg/m³	Point-load strength MN/m²	Porosity %	Absorption %	Saturated sodium sulphate test		Acid resistance
					cycles	% loss	
Binny	2175	1.1	16.2	11.2	10	100	c
Blaxter	2173	1.8	16.5	11.4	15	87	u
Catcastle	2240		9.5		15	55	u
Clashach (standard)	2346	9.0	9.2	5.2	15	0	u
Clashach (coloured)	2007	1.9	22.5	17.1	15	17	u
Corncockle	2130	0.8	18.8	13.1	8	100	c
Corsehill	1990	1.9	22.0	14.8	15	24	c
Cragg	2170	1.4	16.7	12.9			u
Craigleith	2220		13.5	6.8	15	30	u
Craigmillar	2350	3.2	9.2	8.0	12	100	v
Cullalo	2160	2.6	18.4	11.2	15	15	u
Darney	2180	2.0	17.6	10.3	10	100	u
Doddington	2060	1.7	20.2	15.9	15	65	u
Dunhouse	2165		18.4	11.3	15	67	u
Dunmore (new)			17.3		15	23	
Gatelawbridge	2037	1.7	22.6	15.8	8	100	c
Grange	2120	0.7	19.5	15.1	15	57	u
Hailes	2223		14.5	10.9	15	15	u
Hawkhill Wood	2370	3.0	10.1	7.1	15	8	v
Hermand	2210	2.0	15.1	11.2	15	100	u
Lazonby	2260	2.0	13.9	9.1	15	35	c
Locharbriggs	2210	1.5	15.1	11.2	15	100	u
Newbigging	2130	0.6	18.9	12.6	10	100	v
Plean	2180	1.3	17.7	14.4	6	100	u
Prudham	2150		19.4	11.8	15	70	u
Ravelston	2630	3.8	3.6	2.6	15	0	v
Ravelston No. 2	2280	3.1	13.8	8.3	15	11	c
Spittal	2700	16.2	0.5	0.4	15	0	u
Spynie	2070	3.8	17.9	12.2	15	6	u
Stainton	2220	2.0	14.5	9.6	11	100	u
Stancliffe	2240	2.2	12.1	9.2	12	100	u
Stanton Moor	2200	1.2	16.0	13.1	15	83	u
Stoke Hall	2346	2.0	10.5	8.2	15	73	u
Wellfield	2310	3.0	11.9	8.4	15	61	u
Woodkirk	2270	2.2	13.7	11.3	15	82	v

In the above table, 'u' indicates that samples were unaffected by immersion in acid, 'c' that their colour was affected and 'v' that samples from the same quarry yielded variable results, ranging from unaffected to complete disintegration.

Historic values have been omitted from this summary because of differences between modern and historic test procedures. See Appendix 5b for further information.

APPENDIX 5 Properties of building stones: B. Localities, descriptions and properties of building stones

INTRODUCTORY NOTES

1. The data in this appendix are given to enable a comparison to be made between stones. Differences in values for the same stone are to be expected because of
   (a) natural variations in the stone from any one quarry,
   (b) differences in test procedures.
2. Data for which a reference is not stated were derived for this text at Napier University, Edinburgh. These data have been supplemented using test results from other sources. The historic data were selected from a limited number of well documented sources to provide information on stones for which suitably representative samples are no longer available for testing. Results of relatively recent tests have been reproduced from:
a. Leary E. *The Building Sandstones of the British Isles* (Building Research Establishment), by permission of the Controller, HMSO. Crown copyright 1986. (Abbreviated in text to B.R.E.)
b. Davey, A., Heath, B., Hodges, D., Milne, R., Palmer, M., *The Care and Conservation of Georgian Houses - A Maintenance Manual for the New Town of Edinburgh*, 1978, by permission of the Edinburgh New Town Conservation Committee, using data from tests by G.M. and K.M.M. Walkden. (Abbreviated in the text to ENTCC)
3. A bibliography is given in Appendix 5c.
4. A Munsell Rock-Color Chart was used for colour determination.
5. Texture is based upon the clast (particle) sizes of the BGS grain-size scheme (Table 2.1).

Binny

Locality:	Uphall, West Lothian
	NT 057730
Geological Period:	Lower Carboniferous
Colour:	pale yellowish brown
Texture:	fine to medium-grained
Bulk density:	2160 kg/m³ (Beare 1891)
	2175 kg/m³
Crushing Strength:	24.4 MN/m²
Point-load strength:	1.1 MN/m²
Water absorption:	12.2% (Bloxam 1857)
	11.2%
Apparent porosity:	15.7% (Bloxam 1857)
	16.2%
Acid immersion test:	discoloured, otherwise unaffected
Sodium sulphate crystallisation test (saturated):	disintegrated after 10 cycles

Blaxter

Locality:	Elsdon, Otterburn
	NY 931873
Geological Period:	Lower Carboniferous
Colour:	yellow grey, flecked moderate yellowish brown
Texture:	fine to medium-grained
Bulk density:	2173 kg/m³
Crushing Strength:	57.1 MN/m² (ENTCC)
Point-load strength:	1.8 MN/m²
Water absorption:	11.4%
Apparent porosity:	16.5%
Acid immersion test:	unaffected
Sodium sulphate crystallisation test (saturated):	87% loss in mass after 15 cycles

Catcastle

Locality:	Lartington, Barnard Castle
	NZ 015165
Geological Period:	Lower Carboniferous
Colour:	yellowish grey, flecked greyish yellow
Texture:	medium-coarse
Bulk density:	2240 kg/m3
Water absorption:	9.5%
Acid immersion test:	unaffected
Sodium sulphate crystallisation test (saturated):	55% loss in mass after 15 cycles

Clashach

Locality:	Hopeman, Moray
	NJ 162701
Geological Period:	Upper Permian

Note: this quarry yields two distinctively different types of stone, the properties of each are stated.
'Standard'

Colour:	greyish orange
Texture:	fine-grained
Bulk density:	2346 kg/m³
Crushing Strength:	85.8 MN/m² (ENTCC)
Point-load strength:	9.0 MN/m²
Water absorption:	5.2%
Apparent porosity:	9.2%
Acid immersion test:	unaffected
Sodium sulphate crystallisation test (saturated):	no loss in mass after 15 cycles

'Coloured'

Colour:	streaked yellowish orange to yellowish brown
Texture:	fine-grained
Bulk density:	2007 kg/m^3
Point-load strength:	1.9 MN/m^2
Water absorption:	17.1%
Apparent porosity:	22.5%
Acid immersion test:	unaffected
Sodium sulphate crystallisation test (saturated):	17% loss in mass after 15 cycles

Corncockle

Locality:	Lochmaben, Dumfries& Galloway
	NY 086870
Geological Period:	Permian
Colour:	pale red
Texture:	fine to medium-grained
Bulk density:	2130 kg/m^3
Crushing Strength:	41.2 MN/m^2 (Beare 1891)
Point-load strength:	0.79 MN/m^2
Water absorption:	13.1%
Apparent porosity:	18.8%
Acid immersion test:	colour reduced to creamy brown
Sodium sulphate crystallisation test (saturated):	disintegrated after 8 cycles

Corsehill

Locality:	Annan
	NY 206700
Geological Period:	Triassic
Colour:	pale red
Texture:	fine-grained
Bulk density:	2090 kg/m^3 (Beare 1891)
	1990 kg/m3
Crushing Strength:	47.7 MN/m^2 (Beare 1891)
Point-load strength:	1.86 MN/m^2
Water absorption:	14.8%
Apparent porosity:	22.0%
Acid immersion test:	some loss of colour
Sodium sulphate crystallisation test (saturated):	24% loss in mass after 15 cycles

Cragg

Locality:	Bellingham, Northumberland
	NY 820850
Geological Period:	Lower Carboniferous
Colour:	very pale orange
Texture:	medium-grained
Bulk density:	2180 kg/m^3 (Beare 1891)
	2170 kg/m^3
Crushing Strength:	61.5 MN/m^2 (Beare 1891)
Point-load strength:	1.4 MN/m^2
Water absorption:	12.9%
Apparent porosity:	16.7%
Acid immersion test:	unaffected

Craigleith

Locality:	Edinburgh
	NT 226745
Geological Period:	Lower Carboniferous
Colour:	very pale orange
Texture:	very-fine-grained
Bulk density:	2220 kg/m^3 (Beare 1891)
	2220 kg/m^3 (ENTCC 1978)
Crushing Strength:	93.9 MN/m^2 (Beare 1891)
	94.3 MN/m2 (ENTCC 1978)
Water absorption:	6.8% (ENTCC 1978)
Apparent porosity:	13.5% (ENTCC 1978)
Acid immersion test:	unaffected (ENTCC 1978)

Sodium sulphate crystallisation test (saturated): 30% loss in mass after 15 cycles (ENTCC 1978)

Craigmillar

Locality:	Edinburgh
	NT285709
Geological Period:	Lower Carboniferous
Colour:	light brownish grey
Texture:	fine- to medium-grained
Bulk density:	2350 kg/m^3
Crushing Strength:	43.9 MN/m^2

Point-load strength:	3.2 MN/m²
Water absorption:	8.0%
Apparent porosity:	9.2%
Acid immersion test:	highly variable
Sodium sulphate crystallisation test (saturated):	disintegrated after 12 cycles

Cullalo

Locality:	Fife
	NT 184874
Geological Period:	Lower Carboniferous
Colour:	yellowish grey
Texture:	very-fine to fine-grained
Bulk density:	2160 kg/m³
Crushing Strength:	35.7 MN/m²
Point-load strength:	2.6 MN/m²
Water absorption:	11.2%
Apparent porosity:	18.4%
Acid immersion test:	unaffected
Sodium sulphate crystallisation test (saturated):	15% loss in mass after 15 cycles

Darney

Locality:	West Woodburn, Northumberland
	NY 910870
Geological Period:	Lower Carboniferous
Colour:	light yellowish grey
Texture:	fine-grained
Bulk density:	2180 kg/m³
Crushing Strength:	32.0 MN/m²
Point-load strength:	2.0 MN/m²
Water absorption:	10.3%
Apparent porosity:	17.6%
Acid immersion test:	unaffected
Sodium sulphate crystallisation test (saturated):	disintegrated after 10 cycles

Doddington

Locality:	Wooler, Northumberland
	NU 008326
Geological Period:	Lower Carboniferous
Colour:	light brownish grey

Texture:	fine-grained
Bulk density:	2060 kg/m³
Crushing Strength:	23.2 MN/m²
Point-load strength:	1.7 MN/m²
Water absorption:	15.9%
Apparent porosity:	20.2%
Acid immersion test:	unaffected

Sodium sulphate crystallisation test (saturated): 65% loss in mass after 15 cycles; negligible loss after 15 cycles (B.R.E. 1986)

Dunhouse

Locality:	Staindrop, County Durham
	NZ 114195
Geological Period:	Upper Carboniferous, Millstone Grit
Colour:	yellowish grey
Texture:	fine-grained
Bulk density:	2165 kg/m³
Water absorption:	11.3%
Apparent porosity:	18.4%
Acid immersion test:	unaffected

Sodium sulphate crystallisation test (saturated): 67% loss in mass after 15 cycles

Dunmore (new quarry)

Locality:	Cowie, near Stirling
	NS 859882
Geological Period:	Upper Carboniferous
Colour:	yellowish grey
Texture:	medium-grained
Apparent porosity:	17.3% (B.R.E. 1986)
Acid immersion test:	passed (B.R.E. 1986)

Sodium sulphate crystallisation test (saturated): between 0 and 47% loss in mass after 15 cycles (B.R.E. 1986)

Gatelawbridge

Locality:	Thornhill, Dumfries & Galloway
	NX 902965
Geological Period:	Permian
Colour:	moderate reddish brown
Texture:	very-fine-grained

Bulk density:	2037 kg/m³
Crushing Strength:	16.7 MN/m²
Point-load strength:	1.7 MN/m²
Water absorption:	15.8%
Apparent porosity:	22.6%
Acid immersion test:	loss of colour, otherwise unaffected
Sodium sulphate crystallisation test (saturated):	disintegration after 8 cycles

Grange

Locality:	Burntisland, Fife
	NT 223867
Geological Period:	Lower Carboniferous
Colour:	very light brownish-grey
Texture:	fine-grained
Bulk density:	2120 kg/m³
Crushing Strength:	18.2 MN/m²
Point-load strength:	0.7 MN/m²
Water absorption:	15.1%
Apparent porosity:	19.5%
Acid immersion test:	unaffected
Sodium sulphate crystallisation test (saturated):	57% loss in mass after 15 cycles

Hailes

Locality:	Edinburgh
	NT 208706
Geological Period:	Lower Carboniferous
Colour:	pinkish to light brownish grey
Texture:	fine-grained; commonly showing thin, wavy, dark-coloured laminations
Bulk density:	'white' 2304 kg/m³ (Beare 1891)
	'white' 2295 kg/m³ (Beare 1891)
	'grey' 2223 kg/m³
Crushing Strength:	'white' 72.1 MN/m² (Beare 1891)
	'blue' 50.1 MN/m² (ENTCC 1978)
Water absorption:	10.9%
Apparent porosity:	14.5%
Acid immersion test:	unaffected
Sodium sulphate crystallisation test (saturated):	15% loss in mass after 15 cycles

Hawkhill Wood

Locality:	Craigmillar, Edinburgh
	NT 291711
Geological Period:	Lower Carboniferous
Colour:	light brownish-grey
Texture:	fine-grained
Bulk density:	2370 kg/m^3
Crushing Strength:	42.8 MN/m^2
Point-load strength:	3.0 MN/m^2
Water absorption:	7.1%
Apparent porosity:	10.1%
Acid immersion test:	varies from unaffected to completely disintegrated
Sodium sulphate crystallisation test (saturated):	8% loss in mass after 15 cycles

Hermand

Locality:	West Calder, West Lothian
	NT 029635
Geological Period:	Lower Carboniferous
Colour:	light-olive to greenish-grey
Texture:	fine to medium-grained
Bulk density:	2290 kg/m^3 (Beare 1891)
	2210 kg/m^3
Crushing Strength:	49.2 MN/m^2 (Beare 1891)
	22.7 MN/m^2
Point-load strength	2.0 MN/m^2
Water absorption:	11.2%
Apparent porosity:	15.1%
Acid immersion test:	virtually unaffected
Sodium sulphate crystallisation test (saturated):	disintegrated after 15 cycles

Lazonby

Locality:	Lazonby, Penrith
	NY 517380
Geological Period:	Permian
Colour:	pale red
Texture:	medium-grained
Bulk density:	2260 kg/m^3
Point-load strength:	2.0 MN/m^2

Water absorption: 9.1%

Apparent porosity: 13.9%

Acid immersion test: loss of colour, otherwise unaffected

Sodium sulphate crystallisation test (saturated): 35% loss in mass after 15 cycles

Locharbriggs

Locality: Dumfries & Galloway

                                                           NX 990810

Geological Period: Permian

Colour: pale red/light brown

Texture: medium-grained, prominent current-bedding

Bulk density: 2040 kg/m³ (Beare 1891)

                                                           2210 kg/m³

Crushing Strength: 42.3 MN/m² (Beare 1891)

                                                           26.5 MN/m²

Point-load strength: 1.5 MN/m²

Water absorption: 11.2%

Apparent porosity: 15.1%

Acid immersion test: virtually unaffected

Sodium sulphate crystallisation test (saturated): disintegrated after 15 cycles

Newbigging

Locality: Burntisland, Fife

                                                           NT 211864

Geological Period: Lower Carboniferous

Colour: light yellowish grey

Texture: medium-grained

Bulk density: 2130 kg/m³

Crushing Strength: 10.9 MN/m²

Point-load strength: 0.6 MN/m²

Water absorption: 12.6%

Apparent porosity: 18.9%

Acid immersion test: varies from unaffected to disintegrated

Sodium sulphate crystallisation test (saturated): disintegrated after 10 cycles

Note: the mean values stated obscure an unusually wide range of test results on samples from this source.

Plean

Locality:	Stirling
	NS 825861
Geological Period:	Upper Carboniferous
Colour:	very light grey
Texture:	fine-grained
Bulk density:	2220 kg/m³ (Beare 1891)
	2180 kg/m³
Crushing Strength:	65.9 MN/m² (Beare 1891)
Point-load strength:	1.3 MN/m²
Water absorption:	14.4%
Apparent porosity:	17.7%
Acid immersion test:	unaffected

Sodium sulphate crystallisation test (saturated): disintegrated after 6 cycles

Prudham

Locality:	Hexham, Northumberland
	NY 886689
Geological Period:	Lower Carboniferous
Colour:	pinkish grey
Texture:	medium–grained
Bulk density:	2150 kg/m³
Water absorption:	11.8%
Apparent porosity:	19.4%
Acid immersion test:	unaffected

Sodium sulphate crystallisation test (saturated): 70% loss after 15 cycles

Ravelston

Locality:	Edinburgh
	NT 216742
Geological Period:	Lower Carboniferous
Colour:	light olive grey
Texture:	very-fine-grained
Bulk density:	2630 kg/m³
Crushing Strength:	64.4 MN/m²
Point-load strength:	3.8 MN/m²
Water absorption:	2.6%
Apparent porosity:	3.6%
Acid immersion test:	variable, slight surface pitting

Sodium sulphate crystallisation test (saturated): no loss in mass after 15 cycles, but fissures opening in samples

Ravelston 'Black'

Note: named after an unusual but unrepresentative bed of black sandstone which was not tested.

Locality:	Edinburgh
	NT 212736
Geological Period:	Lower Carboniferous
Colour:	light brownish grey/light grey
Texture:	very-fine-grained
Bulk density:	2280 kg/m³
Crushing Strength:	56.8 MN/m²
Point-load strength:	3.1 MN/m²
Water absorption:	8.3%
Apparent porosity:	13.8%
Acid immersion test:	slightly bleached, otherwise unaffected

Sodium sulphate crystallisation test (saturated): 11% loss in mass after 15 cycles

Spittal

Locality:	Spittal, near Thurso
	ND 172542
Geological Period:	Middle Devonian
Colour:	dark grey
Texture:	silty, laminated
Bulk density:	2700 kg/m³
Point-load strength:	16.2 MN/m²
Water absorption:	0.4%
Apparent porosity:	0.5%
Acid immersion test:	unaffected

Sodium sulphate crystallisation test (saturated): negligible loss in mass after 15 cycles

Spynie

Locality:	Elgin, Moray
	NJ 222657
Geological Period:	Upper Triassic
Colour:	yellowish grey
Texture:	very-fine-grained
Bulk density:	2070 kg/m³
Point-load strength:	3.8 MN/m²
Water absorption:	12.2%
Apparent porosity:	17.9%
Acid immersion test:	unaffected

Sodium sulphate crystallisation test (saturated): 6% loss in mass after 15 cycles

Stainton

Locality:	Stainton, Co Durham
	NZ 070189
Geological Period:	Upper Carboniferous, Millstone Grit
Colour:	very pale orange, streaked greyish to dark yellowish orange
Texture:	fine-grained
Bulk density:	2220 kg/m^3
Crushing Strength:	48.0 MN/m^2 (ENTCC 1978)
	27.0 MN/m^2
Point-load strength:	2.0 MN/m^2
Water absorption:	9.6%
Apparent porosity:	14.5%
Acid immersion test:	unaffected
Sodium sulphate crystallisation test (saturated):	disintegrated after 11 cycles

Stancliffe

Locality:	Darley Dale, Matlock
	SK 267638
Geological Period:	Upper Carboniferous, Millstone Grit
Colour:	yellowish grey, speckled
Texture:	fine- to medium-grained
Bulk density:	2240 kg/m^3
Crushing Strength:	33.4 MN/m^2
Point-load strength:	2.2 MN/m^2
Water absorption:	9.2%
Apparent porosity:	12.1%
Acid immersion test:	unaffected
Sodium sulphate crystallisation test (saturated):	disintegrated after 12 cycles

Stanton Moor

Locality:	Birchover, near Matlock
	SK 242624
Geological Period:	Upper Carboniferous, Millstone Grit
Colour:	greyish orange pink, but variable, even within the same block
Texture:	fine- to medium-grained
Bulk density:	2200 kg/m^3

Point-load strength:	1.2 MN/m²
Water absorption:	13.1%
Apparent porosity:	16.0%
Acid immersion test:	unaffected
Sodium sulphate crystallisation test (saturated):	83% loss in mass after 15 cycles

Stoke Hall

Locality:	Eyam, Derbyshire
	SK 237770
Geological Period:	Upper Carboniferous, Millstone Grit
Colour:	very pale orange
Texture:	fine-grained
Bulk density:	2346 kg/m³
Crushing strength:	70.0 MN/m² (supplied by Stoke Hall)
Point-load strength:	2.0 MN/m²
Water absorption:	8.2%
Apparent porosity:	10.5%
Acid immersion test:	unaffected
Sodium sulphate crystallisation test (saturated):	73% loss in mass after 15 cycles

Wellfield ('Crossland Hill York Stone')

Locality:	Crosland Hill, Huddersfield
	SE 118143
Geological Period:	Upper Carboniferous
Colour:	yellowish grey
Texture:	fine-grained
Bulk density:	2310 kg/m³
Crushing strength:	75.5 MN/m²
Point-load strength:	3.0 MN/m²
Water absorption:	8.4%
Apparent porosity:	11.9%
Acid immersion test:	unaffected
Sodium sulphate crystallisation test (saturated):	61% loss in mass after 15 cycles

Woodkirk

Locality:	Morley, Yorkshire
	SE 268263
Geological Period:	Upper Carboniferous

Colour:	greenish grey
Texture:	fine-grained
Bulk density:	2270 kg/m^3
Crushing strength:	59.6 MN/m^2
Point-load strength:	2.2 MN/m^2
Water absorption:	11.3%
Apparent porosity:	13.7%
Acid immersion test:	varies from unaffected (B.R.E.) to expanded and split
Sodium sulphate crystallisation test (saturated):	82% loss in mass after 15 cycles

Appendix 5 Properties of building stones: C. Bibliography

Beare, T.H., Building stones of Great Britain, their crushing strength and other properties, *Proceedings of the Institution of Civil Engineers*, CVII, 1891, p. 341-369.

Bienawski, Z.T., The point-load test in geotechnical practice, *Engineering Geology*, 9, 1975, p. 1-11.

Bloxam, T., On the composition of the building sandstones of Craigleith, Binnie, Giffnock, and Partick Bridge, *Proceedings of the Royal Society of Edinburgh*, 4, 21 December 1857.

Boyle, R., The economic and petrographic geology of the New Red Sandstones of the south and west of Scotland, *Transactions of the Geological Society of Glasgow*, 13, 1909, p. 344-379.

Brown, E.T. (editor)., *Rock characterisation, testing and monitoring; ISRM Suggested Methods*. Pergamon Press, 1981.

Building Research Establishment, The selection of natural building stone, *Digest* 269, 1983.

Craig, G., On building stones used in Edinburgh: their geological sources, relative durability, and other characteristics, *Transactions of the Edinburgh Geological Society*, 6, 1893, p. 254-273.

Gribble, C.D., An assessment of Hopetoun sandstone, *Stone Industries*, July/August 1979.

Honeyborne, D.B. and Harris, P.B., The structure of porous building stone and its relation to weathering behaviour, *Proceedings of the Symposium of the Colston Research Society*, University of Bristol, 10, 1958, p. 343-359.

Howe, J.A., *Geology of building stone*, Edward Arnold, 1910.

Morton, E., The microscopic determination of the strength and durability of building stones. *Engineering*, 24 Sept 1926.

Phemister, J., *Petrographical Report No. 5023*, British Geological Survey, Edinburgh.

Smith, G., Account of the quarries of sandstone in the Edinburgh and Glasgow districts and of the principal slate quarries in Scotland, *Prize Essays and Transactions of the Highland and Agricultural Society of Scotland, (New Series)*, 4, 1835, p. 81-97.

Warnes, A.S., *Building stones, their properties, decay, and preservation*, London: Ernest Benn Ltd, 1926.

Watson, J., *British and foreign building stones*, Cambridge: Cambridge University Press, 1911.

APPENDIX 6 Fossil trees from Craigleith, Granton and Redhall Quarries

Between 1826 and 1873, several fossil trees were removed from Craigleith Quarry. Most are representatives of the genus *Pitus* (*Pitys*) of the Family *Lyginopteridaceae*.[1] The first recorded tree was 8.6m long and had a diameter of 0.9m. The second, discovered in 1830 and described by Henry Witham,[2] was 14m long and 1.8m thick at its widest. In 1834, members of the then recently formed British Association for the Advancement of Science, when it met in Edinburgh, joined the crowds which flocked to see the tree.[3] A large part of it was sent to the Royal Botanic Garden. It can still be seen outside the Palm House. The third with dimensions of 7.3m by 3m (maximum diameter) was discovered in about 1840 and was eventually (1854) removed to Rockville, a villa at Murrayfield. A smaller tree was found during the 1840s and removed to the grounds of Barnton House. The fifth tree first appeared in 1854 and was partly removed but then lost until the 1870s when the Hon. Vice-President of the Royal Society of Edinburgh secured the removal of 12.2m to the British Museum (later to become the Natural History Museum) in London. Part of this piece was later erected in the Museum grounds where it remains to this day, although much weathered. With a girth of 4m, this specimen was described at the time as 'by far the most remarkable relic of Palaeozoic vegetation known'.

Two further pieces were discovered in about 1873. One was a trunk, and about 1.8m of it was divided up and sent to the Royal Botanic Garden, the Museum of Science and Art (now the National Museums of Scotland) and the British Museum. The other discovery was of a smaller piece, thought to be a branch, 2.4m long. Six of these trees and two other fragments were found close together in the west end of the quarry at depths between 30.5m and 54.8m. Some of them were flattened, others were cylindrical in section. The sandstone near these fossils was known by the quarrymen as 'bastard whin' and was unsuitable for building, being tougher and more easily discoloured than the rest of the 'liver' rock. It was suggested that, since the trees had no branches, they had been carried to their final resting places by flood waters which had stripped their branches and dumped them with a mass of sand, or that they had fallen into quick sands. Since they are so well preserved it is likely that they were buried rapidly before the wood had time to rot.[4]

Craigleith Quarry also yielded many less spectacular plant remains. Of these the most interesting were pieces of Lepidodendron, found in the 1890s towards the end of the quarry's active life.[5] The largest of these was a slightly flattened piece of trunk, 0.35m across and over 0.91m long lying parallel to the bedding of the sandstone. When this was being removed from the matrix it was found to contain four pockets of brown-coloured deposit which contained what were considered to be freshwater gastropod shells. These were probably carried into the tree trunk as it lay rotting in a river before it was finally buried in the sediment.

Craigleith Sandstone was also worked at the northern end of the Granton Dome in several quarries, notably Granton Sea Quarry and Granton Land Quarry. Stone from Granton was described as hard and cream-coloured.[6] During work in the Sea Quarry, some time about 1839, two fossil trees of the genus *Pitus* were uncovered. One was 'high and inaccessible' in the inside face of the west wall of the quarry. The other, larger specimen was left lying on a pedestal of stone in the middle of the quarry as it was too heavy to be moved.[7] The larger one was 22.9m long and was a sufficiently important feature of the quarry to warrant inclusion on the 1853 Ordnance Survey map.

At one of the quarries at Redhall many fossil plants were discovered including sandstone casts and one large fossil tree like those found at Craigleith and Granton. Some 3m of this tree, which had a maximum diameter of 2.2m was presented to the Royal Botanic Garden by the lessee of the quarry, Mr James Gowans.[8]

REFERENCES

1. Long, A. G., Observations on the Lower Carboniferous genus Pitus, Witham, *Transactions of the Royal Society of Edinburgh*, 70, 1979, p. 111-127.

2. Witham, H., A description of a fossil tree, *Transactions of the Royal Society of Edinburgh*, 12, 1834, p.148.

3. Cockburn, H., *Journals*, 1, 1874, p.64.

4. Christison, Sir R., Notice of a fossil tree recently discovered in Craigleith Quarry, near Edinburgh, *Transactions of the Royal Society of Edinburgh*, 27, 1874, p.219.

5. Brown, C., The occurrence of gasteropods (*Platyostomella Scotoburdigalensis*) in a Lepidodendron from Craigleith Quarry, Edinburgh, *Transactions of the Edinburgh Geological Society*, 7, 1899, p.244-251.

6. Craig, G., Building stones used in Edinburgh: their geological sources, relative durability and other characteristics, *Transactions of the Edinburgh Geological Society*, 6, 1893, p.258-259.

7. Christison, Sir R., *op.cit.* , p. 207.

8. Christison, Sir R., *op.cit.*, p.221.

Index

Please note: building numbers in square brackets, e.g. [187], refer to buildings listed in Table 1.1, on pages 8 to 17; locations of these buildings are shown on Figure 1.1, on pages 6 and 7. Figures and Tables are indicated by *italic* page numbers; colour plates, between pages 124 and 125, by prefix "*Pl.*" (e.g. *Pl.* 3 means Plate 3).